American Universities
and Federal Research

American Universities and Federal Research

CHARLES V. KIDD

Foreword by Paul E. Klopsteg

The Belknap Press of Harvard University Press

Cambridge, Massachusetts

1959

Preface

Russia's successful launching of an earth satellite in October 1957 centered attention on the scientific capacity and potentialities of the United States. After the initial shock, moderate confusion, and stress on the importance of demonstrating our ability to make rockets perform dramatic feats, the problem of strengthening our scientific capacity over the long run emerged as a matter of vital concern to the nation.

Our present capacity and particularly our long-range potential in science depend on the intellectual excellence of training from elementary school through graduate school, and on the strength of the drive students have to excel.

The goal of increased national strength in science should not be sought to the exclusion of strength in other fields of learning. Indeed, the fundamental requirements for long-range strength in science — respect for learning in the community, respect for the teacher at all levels, willingness to pay for education of high caliber — will strengthen the social sciences and the humanities.

Among the more general prerequisites to a strong national scientific effort is the attainment of higher standards of excellence by the universities. The impending deluge of students must be accommodated without destroying the capacity of the system as a whole to provide training of the highest quality for all who have the necessary intelligence and incentive. Problems of university financing and staffing which appear to be almost insuperable must be resolved.

The central thesis of this book is that large-scale federal financing of research has set in motion irreversible forces that are affecting the nature of universities, altering their capacity to teach, changing their financial status, modifying the character of parts of the federal administrative structure, establishing new political relations, and changing the way research itself is organized. I believe that the wisdom with which these forces are guided and controlled by the universities and by the federal government will have a major influence not only on the capacity of this nation to defend itself, but on the economic growth of the nation and the preservation of the essential values that underlie our society.

I have expressed opinions when they seemed to be warranted. Whether they are sound or not is of secondary importance. As Lord Keynes observed, "There is no harm in being sometimes wrong, especially if one is promptly found out." What is important is that the questions which they purport to answer be continually probed by competent people, so that if my answers are wrong a sounder set of judgments can be reached.

This book is a product of a term study and travel under a Rockefeller Public Service Award. I have deeply appreciated the opportunity to travel in this country and Europe, and to study for a while at the Graduate School of Public Administration of Harvard University. I am also indebted to my hard-working colleagues at the National Institutes of Health who not only acquiesced in my absence, but insisted that I take time off to write.

All of the judgments are mine. They do not necessarily reflect the opinions of the Department of Health, Education and Welfare, the Public Health Service, or the National Institutes of Health.

It is not possible to name all of those who have given me ideas, facts, insights, criticism, and help of all kinds without which I could not have produced these chapters. Fellow bureaucrats in many agencies have been generous in making data available, in giving up time to read drafts and to write comments. I am particularly grateful to the Staff of the National Science Foundation. A large number of officials and faculty members in this country and in Western Europe either talked with me personally, or answered a questionnaire on training of graduate students. V. O. Key of Harvard University gave me indispensable assistance in reading critically a long and rough manuscript of this book in the form of a doctoral dissertation.

CHARLES V. KIDD

Palais des Nations,
Geneva
March 1959

Contents

Contents

Foreword

The writing of a book such as this is a major enterprise. Its innocent-looking title belies the complexity of interacting relations with which it concerns itself. Were the practice followed today which was customary a century and more ago of amplifying the title of a book with a subtitle, the latter might in the present instance have been: "Being an exposition of the effects of federal financing of research upon the operations of universities and upon the relations between government and the universities."

To undertake an exploration of the subject, and to express views and make comments on its manifold aspects, takes more than determination and courage, particularly in view of the diversity of attitudes toward the problems which it harbors. It requires also specialized interest in and understanding of the research function of our system of higher education, and of the relation of this function with those others which together comprise the traditional obligations of the university to the public. It calls for appreciation of the historic background of government in science and insight into the present-day deep involvement of its agencies in science and technology. Moreover, these interests must have associated with them analytical ability, a philosophical outlook, and facility of expression.

The author of this volume is qualified, as few persons would be, to deal with the many aspects of government-university relations, especially with those arising from the ever-increasing funds out of which research services are procured and grants made to universities. In his professional work he has had much experience in some of the activities which he discusses. The result of his painstaking, thoughtful work can help provide direction to the rapidly evolving mutual give-and-take between government and the universities which has been going on since World War II.

It has long been apparent that the burgeoning funds issuing from the federal treasury have greatly altered the pattern if not the nature of research done by members of university faculties.

There is neither question nor argument that the support provided to university research over the years since 1945 has, in the main, been beneficial and that much good research has resulted, the results of which have been published in the appropriate journals. It is true also that the exponentially increasing funds have in some cases required almost revolutionary changes in organization to cope with the new problems. The availability of federal funds for research has, in short, profoundly affected many institutions. Among some scientists and administrators the effect has been to induce a sense of ease because of the prospects of securing plenty of money to finance all kinds of research. Others have misgivings over the hazard to freedom of inquiry which might develop with constantly increasing government subsidization.

Apprehension over government interference with university affairs is shared by many members of university staffs and persons outside the universities who regard the institutions as our one instrumentality for the development of our most valuable, our intellectual, resources. To one who has seen at first hand some of the less desirable consequences of the new relations between government and the universities the misgivings appear well founded.

Certainly one of the most disturbing among them is the ready acceptance by some institutions of the restrictions and onerous requirements imposed by some procurement contracts for research services. Should not an institution, steeped in the traditions of learning and scholarship, in its own best interests avoid contractual responsibilities for services the propriety of which as a university operation may be questioned? Although the restrictions are less onerous under grants made to assist institutions in their support of scholarly endeavors of the faculty, some measure of control or direction cannot be avoided in the process by which funds are allocated and disbursed.

The readiness if not the eagerness with which federal funds are not only accepted but sought, notwithstanding the restrictions, is easily understood. The universities need the funds, and it is their responsibility to obtain them by all honorable and legitimate means. An unanswered question is whether methods can be devised which would remove all possibility of bureaucratic intrusion through the channels in which federal money flows to the uni-

versity. Significantly, the author cites many examples of interference with normal operations in universities which occur when
government enters the picture. His optimism on this question may
not be widely shared.

As the author points out, the problems arising in the administration of research in the universities are not the only ones generated by funds from the federal treasury. There are great problems
of warping and distortion of the educational pattern which would
be avoided if the institutions could obtain uncommitted funds to
finance both their day-to-day operations and their capital expenditures. The problems become more acute with the rising costs that
accompany increasing pressures from rapidly expanding college
populations. Nor are they lessened in the light of the historical
position held by government against federal subsidy for higher
education, and of the large funds now provided for but one of
the functions of the university, namely research and development
in the sciences.

Moreover, insofar as basic research and the educational process are closely interrelated, and insofar as the liberal arts college
has responsibility for higher education, as does the university, any
solution of the problems between government and the university
cannot ignore the undergraduate liberal arts college as an important part of the picture.

Dr. Kidd skillfully handles the major issues. He provides information obtained through study and through interviews and
answers to questionnaires. He expresses views and makes comments where they are indicated. All are offered in a logical ex-
pository structure which develops the reader's understanding and
appreciation of the problems.

Every university administrator and every research scientist
who has, or thinks he should have, government support, and every
government official with responsibility for decisions affecting the
disbursement of funds to universities, will find the substance of
the author's presentation stimulating, and his comments provoca-
tive of serious thought. The problems which arise in the joint
efforts of the government and the universities to increase our national competence in science and technology, while keeping the
universities intellectually vigorous and administratively independ-

ent, are deserving of the earnest attention of any interested person. This book will prove most helpful to those who think seriously about such questions.

PAUL E. KLOPSTEG

American Universities and Federal Research

1

Research Goals of Federal Agencies

We are living through an accelerating scientific revolution that leaves no aspect of our culture untouched. The applications of science introduce change, as well as the expectation of change, as a major premise of social, economic, and political life. What the full implications of the accelerating rate of change will be upon people as individuals and people in groups remain to be seen. One of the obvious consequences of the partial mastery of nature through science is to make meaningful the question, whether man will use science to annihilate himself. This question emerged with great clarity after the fall of 1957 when Russian rockets and other scientific and technological advances illuminated with a great glare some of our deficiencies as a nation. The shock generated by the Russian accomplishments gave rise to a reappraisal not only of military strength and strategy, but of foreign policy, and of our system of education and national science policy as well. It is likely that as long as we survive, science will continue to exert a pervasive revolutionary force upon our society.

In the enormously complex set of forces through which the relations between science and society are worked out, universities and the federal government play central roles. ("University" is used throughout this book as synonymous with "institution of higher education," except where a specific distinction is drawn between colleges and universities. About 95 percent of all federal research and development contracts with institutions of higher education are with universities.) Universities provide a major

1

site for research. Without them the nation would have few scientists of any kind. More important perhaps is the universities' role as guardian and disseminator of the great thought systems of Western culture, our views on the nature of the rights and obligations of individuals, the nature, purpose and limits of the state, and the relation between the individual and the state. Most important, the university at its best is a key institution through which the right of man to know and to seek knowledge freely is safeguarded. It is through remaining free to preserve knowledge, to probe and to criticize our culture, our economy and our political system that universities can best serve the nation as a world power.

Our national welfare depends on the wisdom with which the affairs of the federal government are managed, for it seems destined by irresistible forces to play a larger role in every significant aspect of our national life. Primarily through the constitutional responsibility to provide for the common defense, an unprecedented share of the national income is devoted to paying for the wars of the past and for the defense of the present and future. The defense of the nation depends on technological superiority. And in the long run, technological superiority must rest on scientific superiority. The nation's technological and scientific potential rests upon the capacity of a relatively small group of scientists and engineers. The federal government and the nation depend on universities both as sites for research and as training institutions.

Science thrusts research to the fore not only as a means of national defense but also as a means of providing for the general welfare. Research in agriculture, biology, medicine, meteorology, air transportation, road building, food standards and every other activity of the federal government is conducted in federal laboratories, or financed in other laboratories with federal funds. As the President's Science Advisory Committee reminded him forcibly, late in 1958: "In the 13 years since the end of World War II, science and technology have pushed to the forefront of national life with an urgency that no Congress or President serving in the first four decades of this century could have imagined." [1]

The needs and purposes of these two central institutions in our national life inevitably throw them together. The federal govern-

2

ment needs universities to carry out work which must be done there. It is also an agent for the nation in ensuring that science thrives in universities apart from the needs of government. The universities need the federal government because all other sources of support put together are not sufficient to give the nation the university system which it needs. How federal participation is to be achieved without federal domination is the problem. This chapter describes the federal research programs, and particularly those aspects which affect universities. In the second chapter, the commonly accepted functions of universities are outlined and the problem of reconciling the functions of the federal government and the universities is presented.

Research objectives of federal agencies

We live under a government of laws, and the research activities of all the federal agencies are made possible by grants of authority contained in statutes.

About 90 percent of all federal funds for research and development and 99 percent of the federal research funds for research in universities are provided under the statutory research charters of five agencies: the Department of Agriculture, the Public Health Service, the National Science Foundation, the Atomic Energy Commission, and the Department of Defense.

The Department of Agriculture was authorized by the Hatch Act of 1887 "to promote scientific investigation and experiment respecting the principles and applications of agricultural science." In 1933 the Department was authorized to support research "into laws and principles underlying basic problems of agriculture in its broadest sense," and to support research relating to the development of new uses and markets for agricultural products. The Public Health Service Act of 1946 states that the service shall "encourage . . . scientific institutions, and scientists in the conduct of . . . research investigations, experiments, demonstrations, and studies relating to the causes, diagnosis, treatment, control and prevention of physical and mental diseases and impairments of man." The National Science Foundation was authorized in 1950 to "initiate and support basic scientific research in the mathematical, physical, medical, biological, engineering and other sciences by making contracts and other arrangements including grants, loans, and other forms of assistance."

Like the civilian agencies many of the defense departments have very general congressional mandates to finance research. As one example, the Office of Naval Research has authority (P.L. 586, 1946) "to plan, foster and encourage scientific research in recognition of its paramount importance as related to the maintenance of future naval power and the preservation of national security."

The role of the federal government in supporting research cannot be adequately understood without taking into account the development of the National Science Foundation, its specific functions, and its place among the other federal research agencies. The National Science Foundation Act of 1950 authorizes and directs the Foundation:

> to develop and encourage the pursuit of a national policy for the promotion of basic research and education in the sciences;
> to initiate and support basic scientific research in the mathematical, physical, medical, biological, engineering, and other sciences . . . and to appraise the impact of research upon industrial development and upon the general welfare . . .
> to award . . . scholarships and graduate fellowships . . .
> to evaluate scientific research programs undertaken by agencies of the Federal Government, and to correlate the Foundation's scientific research programs with those undertaken by individuals and by public and private research groups . . . (Section 3 of Public Law 507, 81st Congress)

In summary, the Act sets two broad tasks. One, supporting basic research and training scientists. Two, developing broad policy and coordinating the work of the Foundation's programs with those of other public and private organizations.

A central characteristic of all of the research statutes is the breadth and generality of the authority which they grant to the executive agencies. This aspect of the laws is so important that it is dealt with in detail below.

Another significant characteristic of federally financed research is that most of it is administered by operating organizations whose primary function is not research. When a federal agency has mixed objectives, the departmental effort must be to

4

secure the most effective balance between research and other functions. Representatives of universities sometimes approach questions raised by federal financing of research with the assumption that the federal agency can resolve the problem solely in terms of government-university relations and the requirements for productive research. This is rarely the case, and federal officials sometimes do not or cannot explain to universities why other considerations influence their decisions.

Finally, each federal agency acts with a high degree of autonomy in financing research. As the President's Science Advisory Committee reported to him in December 1958: "Each agency and department continues to formulate its own policies in science and technology with insufficient reference to the policies of others." [2] As a result, the federal government as a whole has had only very vague research policies and objectives. What the federal government is trying to do is simply the sum of the objectives of the various agencies. But so far as universities are concerned, the total effect of research funds provided by all federal agencies cannot be adequately assessed by looking separately at the effects of each segment. The total volume of federal research funds has repercussions, for example, on the availability of the faculty for teaching, on the funds available for research in the arts and humanities, and on the values and objectives of the faculty and students.

Purchase and support of research

To attain the various ends sought by research, the federal agencies use two means — the *purchase* of research and the *support* of research. Both purchase and support are directed towards the same ultimate objective — furtherance of the national interest. These two means serve the national interest, as contrasted with the more narrowly defined interests of federal agencies or of universities, in different ways and the distinction is a significant one. The term "supported research," for example, implies aid to universities to advance research of interest to faculty members as distinguished from research of value to the nation as a whole. Many persons feel that when the federal government supports research it simply helps universities to do what they should be doing anyway; others, with whom I agree, hold that the federal government

5

supports research in universities not to help the universities and individual scientists but to ensure that an activity of great value to the nation as a whole is not neglected.

Even though purchase and support are not always distinct in practice, the differences between them are meaningful and useful. In principle the federal government acts in different capacities when it purchases and when it supports research. When it purchases research, the federal government is pursuing an activity necessary to the effective functioning of the government as an operating entity.

Some of these functions, such as national defense, are reserved to the federal government. In contrast, when research is supported, the federal government is providing the means for more effective performance of a productive function but not necessarily one performed by federal agencies. In this capacity, the agencies are patrons of science, a role quite different in concept from that of using science to make more effective the various direct operating functions of the federal government.

Whether research is purchased or supported determines who takes the initiative in proposing research. When it is purchased, the initiative lies with the purchaser. The purchasing agency first defines the problem it wishes to have solved and then seeks someone willing to solve it. The purchasing agency uses universities and their faculties essentially as it would use the resources of an industrial research organization. If the objective of the federal agency is to support and strengthen a field of science, however, initiative rests with the investigator. He indicates to the supporting agency what he wants to do. The supporting agency then assesses the investigator himself as well as what he proposes to do and decides whether support is warranted.

Whether the objective of an agency is the support or the purchase of research also determines the relative weight given to the operating needs of the agency as contrasted with the needs of science and scientists. Support of a field of science is effective only if the most sophisticated judgment is brought to bear upon the relative worth of areas of investigation and investigators. A fine line separates the assignment of reasonable broad scientific priorities from the establishment of confining control over science

6

through centralized decisions. The focus of judgment is on the advancement of a field of learning rather than upon the operating needs of a federal department. For this reason, an agency which supports research must inevitably, if indirectly, consider itself as having the function of strengthening as well as using universities.

When research is purchased, a prime requirement is broad comprehension of the mission of the federal agency and careful attention to the relevance of research to that mission. In research related to defense, for example, research priorities should be based on broad considerations of strategy, assessments of the probability and timing of armed conflict, and the size and location of the conflict. The center of attention is not on a broad area of science but on the needs of a federal department.

Both stability of support and the freedom of the investigator are affected by whether research is supported or purchased. If, for example, an area of science is to be stimulated productively by federal support, the support should be for relatively broad areas of work. Investigators should be free to shift the emphasis of their work as leads develop in the course of research and support should be quite stable to permit them to work on fundamental problems. On the other hand, problems which a federal agency wishes to have solved for its operating needs may be defined as narrowly or as broadly as the nature of the problem indicates. When research is being purchased, the investigator has an obligation to work on the specific task for which he is being paid, and the purchaser need provide funds only until the problem is resolved.

Support of a broad area of science almost inevitably raises questions as to what is involved in the long-run strengthening of an area of science. Two of the most significant of these questions deal with the adequacy of the current corps of investigators, and the prospects for production of competent scientists in adequate numbers. This concern leads naturally to the effect of support of research upon the teaching function of universities and to consideration of other measures designed to increase the number and the competence of the next generation of investigators. Indeed, some agencies which support work proposed by individuals have a broad statutory mandate to train persons for research, to advance research generally, and to support some teaching functions in universities. These agencies show concern for the total effect of federal support of research on the evolution of science and for the over-all goals of colleges and universities. But the most that they can do about them is to attempt to tailor the activities for which they have clear statutory authority so as to be of general assistance to colleges and universities. In general, greater attention can be paid to the over-all needs of universities when research is supported than when it is purchased. But no federal agency has the competence or the authority to view its actions in the light of the total problems of universities. This unsettled state of affairs has repercussions on all aspects of the relation between the federal government and universities. Indeed, the effect of federal research funds on higher education is one of the most significant consequences of the postwar growth of federal research and one of the consequences giving rise to difficult questions of policy.

The clear functional distinction between the support and the purchase of research is not always evident when one views either the activities of specific agencies or the means — contract or grant — that they use in financing research. All federal agencies both purchase and support research in various proportions. The National Science Foundation, for example, although engaged almost entirely in the support of research, purchases some research connected with its responsibilities for measuring the nation's research resources. On the other hand, an element of research support exists even in the parts of the Department of Defense which purchase developmental work on weapons.

The primary administrative devices for federal financing of research — contracts for purchase and grants for support — are often more distinct in form than in substance. Many contracts are not to purchase findings needed by and suggested by a federal agency but to support work initiated by scientists and pursued by them with complete freedom. This is true, for example, of a large proportion of the contracts let by the Office of Naval Research. A few Public Health Service grants, on the other hand, are made to support studies set up under rigid protocols as part of a nationwide planned research program, and investigators willing to take part in these studies are sought out. In short, whether federal research funds reach a university as a contract or as a grant often has little bearing upon whether the individual scientist is doing work at the behest of a federal agency or pursuing his own work with the aid of a federal subsidy.

The fact that the organizational structure of the federal agencies and their mechanisms for financing research tend to hide the functional distinction between support and purchase of research makes preservation of the distinction all the more important. Failure to maintain the functional distinction leads to such common but false beliefs as the idea that the Department of Defense purchases but does not support research, and that contract research necessarily restricts the investigator to a greater degree than research financed by grants.

Breadth of research authority

The breadth of the statutes authorizing the federal agencies to finance research, mentioned briefly above, has various significant consequences for administrators, for scientists, for universities, and for Congress.

Federal agencies have a virtually free hand in determining a number of policies that are as important to universities as the substance of research. The size of grants and contracts, and the extent to which university rather than industrial and other research facilities will be used, are left almost entirely to the executive branch. For example, the statutory research authority of the Atomic Energy Commission is so broadly stated that the Commission has had a free choice as to the proportions of the authorized research which would be conducted in government, university, and industrial laboratories. The Commission chose to rely heavily upon research centers and thereby established by administrative decision, with no specific statutory authority, a form of research organization of great significance to universities.

Indeed, the statutes give administrators more authority in form than they can exercise in substance. Their power of decision is in fact bounded by such things as administrative politics, the judgments of nonpolitical advisers, clientele pressures, and interest groups including universities.

Because the statutes permit decisions of great moment to universities to be made by officials in the executive branch, pressures are created towards close relations between the representatives of universities and federal agencies. It is with administrators rather than with congressmen and senators that universities must deal on questions of such vital importance to them as the relative emphasis on fields of research, and the terms and conditions under which research funds will be made available.

The extreme breadth of the statutory research authority granted to executive agencies has necessitated recapture of a substantial degree of control by the Congress. Science is a force of such power and consequence to the defense and well-being of the nation that the executive branch cannot be given the unlimited authority ostensibly granted by law. The appropriations process, rather than substantive legislation or investigation, is the means by which Congress exerts the most continuing and direct control over the research and development programs of federal agencies. Hearings and reports of House and Senate Committees on appropriations, and the appropriations themselves, are much more important than substantive statutes in controlling not only the size but also the content of the research and development activities of the federal agencies.

Overlapping of research functions

The statutory research mandates of the federal agencies are so broad that several agencies may finance work in the same area of science. Not only is "overlapping" of research possible under the law, it is built into the system. It is entirely possible and proper for the same investigator to be financed simultaneously by, for example, the Atomic Energy Commission, the Office of Naval Research, the National Science Foundation, and the National Institutes of Health.[3]

Not only may a number of agencies finance research in the same field of science, but many agencies support basic research. For example, a large proportion of the grants of the National Science Foundation are for research which might have been financed by other agencies of government if the budgets of other agencies were large enough. Conversely, several agencies support research which insofar as the substance of the research, the motive of the investigator, the prospective applicability of the findings, and the investigator's freedom are concerned is indistinguishable from research supported by the Foundation.[4]

The wide dispersal of financial aid for research among federal agencies reflects fundamental developments in the federal structure for dealing with science over the period 1947–1950. These were the years when the functions of the National Science Foundation were formulated. But during these same years existing federal agencies and an important new one — the Atomic Energy Commission — assumed responsibility for the wartime research programs and then redirected the programs towards meeting peacetime needs. By the time the National Science Foundation first secured a significant budget, in the fiscal year 1952, existing federal agencies were supporting research, including basic research in universities, on an unprecedentedly large scale.

This overlapping of function is not a defect but a fundamental strength of the federal research structure. As Charles Hitch of the Rand Corporation has pointed out: "Under many circumstances the multiple path approach produces results more quickly and more cheaply than attempting to choose the optimal path and concentrating all one's efforts in pursuing it. In research and development . . . there is frequently no substitute for a practice described by that naughtiest of words — duplication . . . There should be more duplication in research and development, the greater is the potential payoff. There should be more, the greater the uncertainty. There should be more, the cheaper is the duplication. These are precisely the results achieved by the profit motive in a competitive economy." [5]

The significance of the rapid and smooth assimilation of extensive scientific activities, particularly those having to do with the support and purchase of research, by the operating parts of the executive branch during and immediately after World War II can hardly be overemphasized as a factor affecting federal science policy. As a consequence of this development one reason for the establishment of a National Science Foundation — to provide funds for basic research — became less urgent between the time the idea of a foundation was first broached and the time the new agency began to make research grants.

11

Centralization and dispersion

The fact that history had in a sense passed the Foundation by gave rise to fundamental questions about the role of the organization in supporting research. Was it to serve as the central arm of the federal government in supporting basic research, a function seen by many as the primary role of the Foundation? Or was its role to be primarily that of filling the gaps left by the activities of other agencies and of supporting research that could not be rationalized as falling within the limits of the statutory authority of other agencies? In short, was the general policy of the federal government to centralize or to disperse support for basic research? There was no statutory answer to this question after the Foundation was established, and no clear statement of the Congress's intention. For example, in discussing the budget of the National Science Foundation on the floor of the Senate on 4 May 1952, Senator H. Alexander Smith of New Jersey had this to say:

> Unfortunately, the previous administration did not give the National Science Foundation the support it required to develop an effective science policy. Our present administration desires to remove the waste and duplication existing as a result of uncoordinated research programs in our various departments. In a letter to me from the Director of the Budget requesting a larger appropriation in fiscal 1954 for the scientific research work, he said: "While this is a substantial increase in the appropriation to the Foundation, it was more than offset by decreases in the justifiable requests of other agencies for similar purposes. These steps were taken in furtherance of the policy of this administration to centralize in the National Science Foundation the Government's programs for support of basic research, which are now carried out by several agencies." [6]

Strong opposition to centralization developed in universities as recorded by the 1954 Report of the Committee on Institutional Research Policy of the American Council on Education:

> The Committee recommends that the Government not concentrate its general-purpose research funds in any single Government agency, since such concentration might result in creating a powerful bureaucracy, which could exercise too much control of education and which might lose the great advantages in research management of diversity in method and objective. [7]

A formal position on centralization of basic research was taken

by the administration in the same year (Executive Order 10,521
— 17 March 1954):

The Foundation shall be increasingly responsible for providing support
by the Federal Government for general-purpose basic research through contracts and grants. The conduct and support by other Federal agencies of
basic research in areas which are closely related to their missions as recognized as important and desirable, especially in response to current national
needs, and shall continue.

The term "general-purpose basic research" was coined to define
basic research not closely related to the operating missions of
federal agencies.

The initial response of the National Science Foundation to the
executive order was not clear, but a forthright and consistent position was formally stated late in 1956:

*The Foundation is guided by the principle that there should not be cen-
tralization of Federal support of direction of basic research in a single agency.*

Centralized responsibility for the administration or direction of all
Government-supported basic research could impede progress through
restriction of freedom of inquiry by scientists and would impose avoidable
difficulties on the agencies that must conduct or support research related to
their respective missions.[8]

This general position was in effect ratified late in 1957 after
Russia fired the first earth satellites. One of the minor consequences of the coup was clear recognition in this country that
scientific training and activities of high caliber and fundamental
significance should be supported from all available sources. Within five weeks after Sputnik I had been fired, the new Secretary of
Defense, Mr. McElroy, signed a new policy on support of basic
research by the Department of Defense. (Department of Defense
Directive 3201.1. Policy on Basic Research, November 12, 1957,
replacing Department of Defense Policy on Basic Research dated
June 19, 1952.) The new directive said:

It is the policy of the Department of Defense:
1. To support a broad and continuing basic research program to assure
the flow of the fundamental knowledge needed by the military departments
as prime users of scientific facts and to evolve novel weapons of war; and
2. To maintain, through such a broad support program, an effective
contact between the military departments and the scientists of the country

so that the military departments are continuously and growingly aware of new scientific developments and the scientists are aware of the military needs.

This was a marked shift in policy, for Mr. McElroy's predecessor had been skeptical of the value of basic research itself, and of the wisdom of conducting or supporting basic research with Department of Defense funds.

In other federal agencies, the specific effect of the sputniks was less pronounced, but the general effect was to confirm the wisdom of dispersal of support for basic research among the agencies.

Money, manpower and facilities

Support of university research by the federal government has for the most part consisted of funds for work in progress. In addition to aiding current research, however, the federal government supplies funds — some of which go to universities — for construction of research facilities and for the training of personnel. While these funds have not been so important to universities as the support of research in progress, they deserve attention because they involve a conceptual extension of the role of the federal government.

Take first the provision of federal funds for construction of university research facilities, amounting to more than half a billion dollars over the period 1947–1957. Explicitly or implicitly, provision of federal funds for research construction rests on the assumption that the federal government has a responsibility to extend the research base of the nation, as well as to ensure effective use of the existing base.

The precise objectives sought by the various agencies in providing research construction funds to universities differ. The Department of Defense and the Atomic Energy Commission have financed research construction to extend the capacity of universities to perform research which these agencies need. Perhaps more significant for universities are the effects of the investment of hundreds of millions of dollars by the Department of Defense and the Atomic Energy Commission in research centers (discussed in Chapter 10) which are remotely associated, or not associated at all, with universities.

Similarly, the National Science Foundation has undertaken to provide funds for large-scale facilities and major equipment when the need is urgent, the technical base sound, and the required funds are not available nor feasibly stimulated from other sources. Under this general policy the Foundation has financed a number of expensive construction and equipment projects, some of which are as important for the concept underlying them as for the funds involved. At present, the Foundation is financing a radio telescope, computation centers, and biological field facilities and equipment for research in high energy physics. The equipment will be available to colleges and universities which cannot provide such facilities out of their own resources. In concept, this represents an extension of the essential idea of the large Department of Defense and Atomic Energy research centers.

Over the period 1957–1959, the Public Health Service administered $90 million in research construction funds for broader purposes. This program was justified on the ground than an extraordinary increase in the nation's total medical research expenditure — from $45 million in 1940 to over $330 million in 1957 — required an expansion in physical facilities for research. Moreover, a group of well-qualified advisers reported to the Secretary of Health, Education and Welfare: "Unless a large construction program designed to expand markedly the facilities of the Nation's system of medical and related schools is undertaken in the immediate future, the total medical research effort of the Nation will be impeded and the number of doctors per 100,000 population will begin to decline in the near future." [9] It should be noted that these construction grants were not for unique or extremely large and expensive facilities, but were designed simply to extend the nation's capacity for medical research. Moreover, the grants were provided with the understanding that the new facilities could be used for teaching as well as for research.

The federal research construction programs have provided unsurpassed material facilities for research in the physical and biological sciences. The splendid physical state of laboratories in the United States and of the instrumentation of these laboratories is largely the consequence of federal research funds.

Federal funds for training research workers are provided

through a number of channels, most of them indirect, and most of the money is paid to individuals rather than to universities. For example, the largest federal program for training at universities, the veterans' education program, is designed to aid a special group, veterans, and not to promote the training of scientists or to aid universities. In fact, an important effect of the program on universities was to throw upon them a teaching burden which if permanent, would have been unbearable. The second largest set of federal training programs, those of the Department of Defense, uses universities to provide specialized training, and general education in the sciences is an incidental and minor effect.

On the other hand, some important educational activities of the federal government are designed specifically to train people in the mathematical, physical, biological, and medical sciences at the graduate or postgraduate level. This is true of the training programs of the National Science Foundation, the Atomic Energy Commission and the National Institutes of Health of the Public Health Service. In 1958, these three agencies spent about $60 million for a variety of educational activities. The National Institutes of Health supplied $33 million to medical and other schools to support training programs related to research and medical service in seven broad categories of disease. Another $6.4 million was disbursed directly to students as fellowships. The National Science Foundation made another $3.2 million available as fellowships and spent almost $10 million on programs for the training of science teachers. These activities are unique because they extend across the board in science, and are not limited to particular fields of knowledge. The training expenditures of the Atomic Energy Commission approximated $5.6 million in 1958. This sum provided for fellowships, other training activities, and equipment — such as special reactors — for training.

As is the case with construction of research facilities, the training activities of these three agencies are designed to expand the research potential of the nation, rather than to make full use of existing potentialities. The evolution of the goal of expansion of the nation's supply of scientists, as contrasted with the use of the existing group most effectively or with the establishment of conditions permitting them to work most effectively, was recognized in 1955 by Mr. Chester Barnard, then Chairman of the National Science Foundation Board:

It seems much clearer now than it did when the National Science Foundation was established that the Federal Government must play an indispensable role in what must be a great and determined national effort . . . It seems clear that the magnitude of the problem is such that the aid of the Federal Government will become increasingly indispensable in the development of an adequate cadre of scientific personnel.[10]

Apart from aid to students, various federal agencies pay universities to undertake special training activities of interest to the agencies. Summer courses for high-school teachers, nationwide cooperative extension work in agriculture and home economics, and professional training for a large number of Department of Defense civilian employees are but a few examples. Such activities are a normal and expected part of the public service activities of many universities and not — with few exceptions — the assumption of a task foreign to the universities' idea of their functions. Finally, federal funds affect the training of scientists in universities importantly through the use of research grant and contract funds to pay research assistants, a matter discussed in detail in Chapter 7.

From this brief discussion of a very complicated subject, it is clear that the federal government has approached aid to students and to universities without a general policy. The federal government does not now have, for example, any such basic aim as the reduction or removal of financial barriers to the higher education of the nation's most gifted young people, or ensuring that educational institutions have, with due regard to local financial responsibilities, a sound financial base.

Extension of the role of the federal government in research through the construction of research facilities and the training of scientists raises an array of policy problems. At what rate should the federal government attempt to expand the nation's research facilities? How much of this expansion should be through universities rather than research institutes or centers, or industrial firms? To what extent should the federal government relieve individuals of their responsibility to finance education? How is a reasonable balance to be achieved between support for research in progress, research facilities, and education of scientists? What are the criteria of balance? How are representatives of universities to participate, if at all, in the discussions and decisions relating to balance?

In answering such questions, the federal government will inevitably become even more involved with the affairs of universities. In order that the federal government be productive in its efforts to expand the research capacity of universities, it must take into account the role of the universities in preserving and transmitting knowledge as well as in their research function.

Structure for policy formation

The research activities of all federal agencies have important effects, including effects upon universities, which cannot be seen clearly by any one agency. These should be assessed in the light of general federal objectives to which the activities of the separate agencies should contribute. General objectives cannot be formulated, the total effects of federal programs cannot be measured and reasonable consistent action by individual agencies cannot be secured by reliance upon their independent activities. A unifying force above the agencies is required.

The Congress has helped to formulate general science policies for the federal government. The great debate over the establishment and functions of the National Science Foundation, for example, was an important contribution to the formation of public opinion. But in the day-to-day operations of Congress, as was noted earlier, both substantive legislation and budgets affecting research are handled in a fragmentary way, even though the consideration given to specific problems is often exhaustive and penetrating. Moreover, the value of the policy function has been at times underestimated and misunderstood in parts of Congress. For example, the National Science Foundation found it difficult during the pre-sputnik era to convey the significance of studies of national research expenditure and of scientific manpower as background for policy. The difficulties are epitomized by these remarks of the chairman of the House Appropriations Subcommittee during the hearing on the 1957 budget of the Foundation:

The first activity is 'National science policy studies.' It may be of some value but are you going to chase rabbits or are you going after big ones?

The program directors are responsible for . . . developing program policies and plans, and for assisting in the development of overall science policy. What do you mean by that language? That certainly ought not to be a recurring item. If you get a good plan, hang on to it.[11]

This skepticism, which had been expressed in earlier years, was followed by a committee report on the proposed budget which said:

The budget estimate for fiscal year 1957 includes $500,000 for making national science policy studies. The Committee reduced the item by $50,000, which is indeed a very small amount, and it will expect the agency to greatly reduce this item next year. Many of these studies are of doubtful value and should be curtailed.[12]

Without overestimating the significance of facts in arriving at decisions on national science policy, the investment of $500,000 a year to secure data on an activity of vital importance to the nation which costs about $10,000,000,000 a year does not seem excessive.

Beginning with the Joint Committee on Atomic Energy, the Congress has gradually strengthened its own structure to deal with questions of national science policy. In 1958, the House of Representatives established a Standing Committee on Science and Astronautics. This is the first time in our history that either house has established a standing committee to deal with science as such. The Senate moved towards the establishment of such a group in 1958 with the creation of the Standing Committee on Astronautics and Space Science.

Greater attention has been paid to the development of a mechanism for formulating general science policies in the executive than in the legislative branch.

The Bureau of the Budget has had a continuing influence not only over the funds proposed in the President's budget, but also over the activities which they finance. Between the end of World War II and the time when the National Science Foundation became fully operative, the Bureau was a primary source of advice to the President on matters involving science policy. It advised the President to veto the first National Science Foundation Act, and the advice was followed. It helped to develop the structure and program of the National Science Foundation immediately after its establishment, and wrote Executive Order 10,521 which made more explicit the general policy and coordinating functions of the Foundation. Finally, the general surveillance of the federal government that is part of the budgetary process has placed the Bureau in a position to coordinate research to a moderate degree.

The Interdepartmental Committee on Scientific Research and Development was established by executive order in 1948, to carry out a recommendation of the President's Scientific Research Board.[13] This Committee, which was dissolved in 1959, as noted below, was a group of federal administrators who dealt with common problems facing federal agencies with substantial research programs. The Committee, as it noted in a report to the President, "performed for the Federal Government as a whole a function similar to that performed by committees and boards established by individual departments and agencies to exercise a coordinating effect among decentralized agencies." [14]

Despite the usefulness of the Committee, however, it was quite properly not asked to answer questions of broad federal policy, nor to coordinate the agencies.

While the Interdepartmental Committee and the Bureau of the Budget were undertaking, in a tentative and partial way, to view the federal science effort as a whole, the proposal to establish a National Science Foundation was being debated. With passage of the National Science Foundation Act in 1950, primary formal responsibility for coordinating the research programs of federal agencies and for developing a national science policy was placed in the National Science Foundation. Expanding and clarifying the Act, an executive order (Number 10,521 – 1954) stated that:

> The National Science Foundation . . . shall . . . recommend to the President policies for the Federal Government which will strengthen the national scientific effort and furnish guidance toward defining the responsibilities of the Federal Government . . . make comprehensive studies and recommendations regarding the Nation's scientific research effort and its resources for scientific activities . . . review the scientific research programs and activities of the Federal Government . . . and shall recommend to the heads of agencies concerning the support given to basic research.

The response of the Foundation was to distinguish between

coordination of the research activities of the federal government and definition of national science policies.

In 1957, the Foundation renounced a formal coordinating role:

The National Science Foundation does not attempt to exercise formal coordinating controls over Federal agencies in the planning or administration of basic research programs."

It would be inappropriate to cast the Foundation in the role of critical coordinator of Federal agencies which support basic research. This would be impractical and unrealistic, especially in the case of large agencies because of their strongly mission-related programs.[15]

This is a realistic conclusion, for the research of federal agencies must be coordinated by an organization with higher status.

The response of the Foundation to the role of policy development — by statute the first obligation placed on the Foundation — has been more positive. As Chester Barnard, former Chairman of the National Science Foundation Board, pointed out in a statement properly ignoring the distinction between basic and applied science:

Only the National Science Foundation . . . has as its exclusive function and reason for existence, leadership for the Government in the promotion of science and the channeling of Government support without any other functions to color its ability to act and to give authoritative advice to the Government and other agencies with respect to government policies and relating to science. These functions are those of leadership rather than direction.[16]

The Foundation has led in the resolution of some difficult national science policy issues. For example, continuing emphasis by the Foundation upon the significance of basic research has been salutary. The educational and training activities of the Foundation have been vigorous and imaginative prototypes for the work of others. The Foundation has moved the federal agencies towards adoption of a uniform policy for payment of the full direct and indirect cost of federal research conducted by universities. It has studied and reported on the relations between government and universities.

All in all, however, the Foundation has not served as the central means for securing answers to the most urgent questions of science policy facing the nation, for reasons inherent in its statutory mission and its administrative status. Most notably, the organization has not been in a position to develop those aspects of science policy which by their nature are the responsibility of the President and his immediate office. The assignment of responsibility for White House functions to an organization outside the White House is explained by the history of the National Science Foundation Act.

When the National Science Foundation was first proposed, the new agency for science was to be given high status by making it almost entirely independent of the President. A bill proposing a super agency to be virtually a fourth branch of government passed Congress and was properly vetoed. The revised bill, which became law, gave the Foundation the status of a major federal agency with clear responsibility to the President, but the organization was not in the Executive Office of the President. The head of the agency, who shares executive authority with the statutory National Science Board, has not been made a member of the cabinet. The fact that the major changes in the status of the Foundation logically required a redefinition of the policy-forming role of the organization was not fully appreciated. Fundamental anomalies were involved in leaving essentially Presidential functions not only outside the Executive Office of the President but in an agency whose head does not have cabinet status.

The fact that the National Science Foundation was not given a status enabling it to handle policy questions requiring resolution in the White House has not been widely recognized, and this gave rise to unwarranted criticism of the Foundation.

Largely as a consequence of the shock administered to the nation by the launching of the first Russian satellite, the rather unsatisfactory structure for consideration of science policy at the top of the executive branch was extensively revamped.

In November 1957 the office of Special Assistant to the President for Science and Technology was created. Dr. James R. Killian, formerly President of the Massachusetts Institute of Technology, was named to the post. The President's Science Advisory Committee, a group which had been established in 1953 but had not been highly influential, was reconstituted. As Dr. Killian pointed out:

Until November 1957, this office never existed in its present form in the

Federal Government, nor had there been, save in wartime, a Science Advisory Committee directly responsible to the President.[17]

The Committee, composed of outstanding scientists from private life, advises the President directly on problems of science which it considers to be significant. It has been well situated to provide advice not only to the President, but also to the National Security Council and the Operations Coordinating Board on broad policy questions relating to research.

After a period of study, the Committee recommended, in *Strengthening American Science, a Report to the President,* the establishment of a Federal Council on Science and Technology. This was done by Executive Order 10,807 on 13 March 1959. This new Council, which replaced the Interdepartmental Committee on Scientific Research and Development, is composed of representatives "of policy rank" from those federal agencies which have important science responsibilities. The tasks of the group are to provide more effective planning and administration of federal research, to identify research needs, to secure better use of scientific resources and to further international cooperation in science. In carrying out these tasks, the Council is directed to consider the effects of federal research on nonfederal programs and institutions, to consider long-range plans for meeting the scientific needs of the federal government, and to consider the effects of nonfederal scientific programs on the federal programs.

Since these broad responsibilities overlapped those of both the Interdepartmental Committee and the National Science Foundation, adjustments were required. The Committee was abolished, but in effect reconstituted as a standing committee, composed of scientist-administrators representing federal agencies, of the new Council. The responsibilities of the National Science Foundation for the development of national science policy were narrowed somewhat, but made more explicit. Executive Order 10,521, which had directed the Foundation to recommend policies "which will strengthen the national scientific effort," was amended to make the Foundation responsible "for the promotion and support of basic research and education in the sciences" and for guidance in defining the responsibilities of the federal government in the conduct not of all research but of basic research.

While the establishment of the Council was perhaps the most significant event relating to the structure of the executive branch for science policy, the adjustments in 1958 and 1959 were more extensive than in any comparable period with the exception of the early years of World War II. As Dr. Killian summarized the changes:

Altogether the year brought an impressive array of organizational innovations for the management of government programs in science and technology and for the provision of scientific advice at policy-making levels. The NASA, the National Aeronautics and Space Council, the Advanced Research Projects Agency, and the new post of Director of Research and Engineering in Defense, the Science Adviser in the State Department, the Special Assistant to the President for Science and Technology, the reconstituted President's Science Advisory Committee, and the newly authorized Federal Council for Science and Technology . . . all these taken together convey the sense of urgency to improve the management and promotion of science by the Federal Government.[17]

The new structure should provide a better means for considering the questions with which this book deals. An administrative hierarchy more realistically related to the hierarchy of policy questions has evolved. The role of the National Science Foundation has been redefined to emphasize basic research and education. The task of dealing with other broad areas of federal science policy, and of reconciling competing goals, has been appropriately placed in the White House.

The fact that the federal government did not develop an entirely satisfactory structure for science policy, including policy toward universities, immediately after World War II, is not surprising. Research has emerged rapidly as a role of the federal government, and the significance of science to the nation has increased rapidly over the past decade. The most significant facts are that the problem is recognized as important in the executive branch and in Congress and that the process of adaptation goes forward.

2

Functions of Universities

The functions of universities determine how they will respond to the tasks urged upon them by federal agencies and to the offers of government to act as a patron to research. Even though diversity is a prime characteristic of the functions and the structure of American universities, they share some common goals. These provide the setting in which federal-university research relations must be worked out.

As an ideal, all American universities carry on the Western European tradition of a company of free scholars. The idea of a university at its best is epitomized in this statement by John D. Millett:

> In the ideal sense of its purpose, a university is a *community of scholars*. It is a community of cooperatively disposed and friendly individuals sharing common ideals and aspirations which unite them in a great cause transcending the boundaries of their separate specialties and capacities. A university is made up of scholars with a devotion to truth as each understands it; ever concerned with broadening the boundaries of man's knowledge, ever willing to share that knowledge with others for their material and spiritual well-being, ever loyal in the service of scholarship, and ever free from any form of tyranny over mind or body.[1]

Four goals

The general form, a community of scholars, is designed to achieve three ends — the preservation, the transmission, and the creation of knowledge. The three goals are inseparable. Each both depends upon and reinforces the others. Maintenance of a

25

normal balance among the three is of major importance to every university. The government's concern with research to the virtual exclusion of the other two functions of universities is the source of an inherent problem in the relation between the federal government and universities.

Apart from the three basic functions, American universities have a strong tradition of service to the community. All public universities feel an obligation to help governments, state and local industries, and economic and social groups solve immediate problems. Private universities also feel such an obligation to various degrees and in various ways. As the President of the California Institute of Technology has said of the Institute:

This, like other privately endowed educational institutions, is simultaneously both a 'private' and a 'public' agency. It is private in the sense that its support comes from the gifts of private individuals and corporations rather than from tax funds. It is public in the sense that it exists only to serve the public welfare through the advancement of education and research. This service to the public welfare is recognized by local, state and national governments through the privilege of tax exemption.[2]

The goal of service, in contrast with the three generally recognized reasons for the existence of universities, does not stem from the Western European tradition, but has grown from American roots. This link with the immediate needs and demands of the state as contrasted with the deeper needs of a society for an institution devoted to the free pursuit of truth, has important consequences for the structure of American universities and for their relations with the federal government.

The extensive involvement of universities with federal research springs in large part from the widespread willingness of private and public universities to undertake tasks for the federal government. This willingness to make university resources available for tasks set by government agencies sharply differentiates American from British and Continental universities. In Europe, most defense and other government research is conducted in government or other laboratories not associated with universities. In the United States, a much larger share of government research has been absorbed into the university structure. Resulting problems range from the need to make minor administrative adaptations to the

26

need to resolve fundamental differences of opinion on the proper relation between the service function and the other three fundamental functions of universities.

In pursuing their goals, American universities exhibit greater adaptability than their European counterparts. The relative emphasis on various objectives shifts with apparent ease. Their administrative structures, a subject reserved for later discussion, seem to change more rapidly in response to new problems than in European and British universities. Their academic hierarchies are less rigid, and they are not hampered by the tradition which prescribes that there be only one full professor in an academic department.

The flexibility of American universities is not always considered a virtue. Some critics maintain that it is not the consequence of adaptability to meet goals rigorously defined and rigorously pursued, but the consequence of intellectual flabbiness and absence of goals. For example, Abraham Flexner attacked the tendency of American universities to establish new organizations for what he considered inadequate reasons.[3] His rage at what he called "the sin of ad-hocness" would certainly be vented even more energetically, and justly in the case of some universities, were he to view the present scene. On the other hand, the ease with which precedents can be broken, new organizations and chairs established, and new areas of study initiated potentially adds a dimension of freedom to the work of individuals and groups in American universities.

Intellectual standards

Whether the full potentialities of American universities can be realized ultimately depends on the level of intellectual standards for teaching and research. It is in this respect that American universities show the greatest diversity.

All universities, even those in which the employer-employee relation between administration and faculty overshadows the concept of a community of scholars in large part reflect the aggregate ability, personalities, and values of faculty members. The standard of excellence set by the faculty as a group is probably the most important single determinant of the impact of federal research

27

funds on universities. This standard of excellence is primary in establishing the essentially social pressures that strongly influence what is done or not done, what is approved or disapproved, what is scorned or admired by faculty members. This intangible force is a much stronger determinant of the quantity and quality of research performed than are written policies and similar formal means of describing or attempting to influence the research policies of universities.

Differences in intellectual standards are reflected in the kind of work most admired by the faculty as a group, the degree of excellence that earns respect, the value placed upon bigness for its own sake, the essential nature of the relation between the university and groups in the community, the competence of graduate students, and the quality of graduate teaching. These differences create the wide disparity in the attitudes of universities toward research financed by the government, the types of research considered suitable for a university, the proportion of university research that should be government-financed, and the appropriate administrative structure for universities.

Even within a single university, standards and values often differ. Most universities are not monolithic structures but groups of schools and departments with different standards. A few universities have a large number of outstanding departments. Many have excellent departments and some that are not so good, and quality typically changes over the years as the faculty changes. In addition, the essential aims of the faculty and of the central administration sometimes differ. For example, the president's office and faculty members often differ sharply on such matters as the volume of research a university should undertake, the need for and means of central review of requests for financial aid for research, and the level in the hierarchy at which research funds should be controlled.

While the quality of a university in large part depends upon the intellectual standards of the faculty, it is by no means easy to assess the actual quality of a university, a department, or faculty members. The judgments are not based on measurable things, but are of the same kind as those called for in assessing a work of art. Nevertheless, these assessments must be made by federal agencies engaged in research. General statements made by people associated with a university are not of much use. It is a rare university president who does not contend that practically all of the research carried on by the faculty is basic. But as a guide to the breadth, the importance, or the quality of the work done by faculties, these words are meaningless. As another example, university officials generally maintain that the university will accept only research grants and contracts that are of interest to the faculty. Many faculties, however, appear to have interests which encompass routine material testing, accumulation of data of little general scientific interest, and similar enterprises. The limit implied by reference to the interests and standards of the faculty is sometimes no limit at all.

The extensive structure of groups advisory to federal research agencies, composed predominantly of scientists drawn from universities, is essentially a device invented to help the agencies arrive at sound judgments on the quality of individual scientists and of universities. In the absence of this elaborate and significant set of advisory relations, there would almost certainly be a smaller proportion of sound administrative decisions.

Research and freedom

While all functions of universities must be considered in reviewing the effect of federal research on universities, the research function is most directly and obviously significant.

Universities do have a unique role in research. As Dr. Vannevar Bush wrote in *Science, the Endless Frontier*:

The university as a whole is charged with the responsibility not only of maintaining the knowledge of the past and imparting it to students but of contributing to new knowledge of all kinds. The scientific worker is thus provided with colleagues who, though they may represent widely differing fields, all have no understanding and appreciation of the value of new knowledge.

The long struggle for academic freedom has provided our universities with the means of protecting the scientist from many of the immediate pressures of convention or prejudice. The university at its best provides its workers with a strong sense of group solidarity and security, plus a substantial degree of personal and intellectual freedom. Both are essential in the development of new knowledge, much of which can arouse opposition because of its tendency to challenge current beliefs and practices.[4]

29

Such statements do not mean that universities have an exclusive franchise to conduct basic research, or that research conducted by individuals not associated with universities is generally inferior. Although these claims are sometimes stated explicitly, it can hardly be seriously maintained that rigorous inquiry into the fundamentals of the physical universe cannot be carried on in research centers, in industrial or government laboratories, or in laboratories supported by private foundations.

In attempting to distinguish the unique role of universities from roles shared with other institutions, the starting point will be an assumption that a major function of universities is to serve as the place where individuals can conduct free inquiries into all aspects of the physical universe and of man as an individual and social animal. By free inquiry is meant a search for knowledge not limited by institutional objectives or external forces.

This view of the function of the university as a means of sustaining freedom of inquiry has many implications for the definition of the research role of universities.

In 1949 the British Department of Scientific and Industrial Research described the research mission of universities, as contrasted with other places where scientists work:

It is generally accepted as essential for the scientific health of any research establishment that it should engage in some fundamental research . . . Usually objective research of this type is not intended to aim at immediate practical results but to gain a better insight into some basic phenomenon such as corrosion, the oxidation of fats, the growth of large molecules, or the electrical state of the upper atmosphere . . . Besides such objective fundamental research there is the equally important field of academic research. Such research is not academic in the sense that it deals with 'pure' science as opposed to 'applied' science. It may involve either or both. It may aim at the discovery of new knowledge for its own sake, or it may be prompted by industrial or social needs. It is academic only in the sense that those who work in this field obey only the spur of intellectual curiosity and should not be expected to follow the practical consequences of the by-products of their work which should be seized upon by others. The best conditions for this type of work are those which prevail at Universities.[5]

Maintenance of freedom as a goal of universities was stressed again in 1957 by the British Advisory Council on Scientific Policy. In its Annual Report for 1956–57, the Council noted: "Although one must recognize that some contract work for government and industry is almost inevitable, in view of the specialized knowledge to be found only in universities, it is essential that this should not be allowed to grow to proportions which would hamper the universities in the free and untrammelled pursuit of knowledge, which is their primary function." [6] In 1955–56 government and industry financed 16 percent of the total recurrent expenditure on scientific research in British universities, as contrasted with about 70 percent from government in this country.

The Advisory Council on Scientific Policy noted that the financing of 16 percent of university research by government and industrial contracts "does not give cause for alarm, but any marked increase would be most undesirable."

It should be noted that the type of general university support provided in Great Britain by the block grant of the University Grants Committee is widely viewed in this country as a threat to the freedom of universities, while in Great Britain the financing of university research by government and industrial contracts on the scale accepted as normal in this country is viewed as a threat to the freedom of universities.

In this country, the Director of the National Science Foundation has pointed out that maintenance of freedom rather than extension of basic research is the essential goal of the university:

> It is in the universities where we must be sure that we uphold the standard of free research. Whether the research is basic or applied, the important thing is that a university is the place where scholars are free to choose what they want to do. In the last analysis this is the best way of insuring maximum progress. One of the most important duties of the universities is to make sure that outside support does not interfere with the freedom of the individual to follow his own choice whether applied research or basic research. [7]

Mees and Leermakers, writing in 1950 primarily of industrial research but with an eye to the governmental and industrial laboratories, reached the same conclusion:

> The preeminence of the universities in scientific work will continue as long as the research work in university departments continues free from any external direction or organization. Compared with other agencies for the prosecution of scientific research — research institutes, technological insti-

tutes, industrial laboratories — universities are at a disadvantage. The investigators are often burdened with administration and with teaching; they are, on the whole, poorly paid; and it is difficult for them to obtain funds for equipment. Clearly, they should not have been able to advance knowledge as rapidly or as widely as the professional research workers of the industrial laboratories or the research institutes. But they are *free* — they can explore unpromising paths and make experiments that any administrator would regard as useless, and sometimes those experiments succeed and those paths lead to new fields of knowledge.[8]*

If this point of view expressed on both sides of the ocean is sound, as I believe it to be, the research function of universities should not be defined as the conduct of basic as contrasted with applied research. A more useful approach would seem to be to define all functions of universities in terms of freedom and, most particularly, the freedom of the individual investigator and teacher.

Maintenance of a uniquely high degree of freedom in universities is in a sense not only desirable but imperative, for this is the prime characteristic distinguishing universities from other research institutions. Universities must sustain freedom as the essential condition of, and indeed the reason for, their existence. They must remain free of domination by any outside group, public or private. They must remain the sole judges of the qualifications of their faculty. They must sustain the conditions under which free intellects may explore where intelligence leads. In this belief, universities seem to present a united front, for the most violent episode to occur in the relations between universities and the federal government was provoked by the government's attempt to control the political views of faculty members.

Freedom is the characteristic which is essential to the conduct of research untrammeled by the boundaries set by institutional goals, and to the production of findings which justify support of universities as centers for the discovery of knowledge. Freedom to learn, freedom to teach, and freedom to seek new knowledge are useful, in a general sense, only if exercise of the freedom produces an excellent product. The major obligations which universities should assume in return for the privilege of providing freedom are the selection of faculty members of high ability and the crea-

* By permission from *The organization of industrial scientific research*, by Mees and Leermakers. 1950. McGraw-Hill Book Co., Inc.

tion of an institutional environment into which are built strong and effective pressures to produce. It is hard to conceive of a set of conditions better calculated to drive people to the limit of their capacities than those existing in a university in which excellence is taken for granted.

The university is a uniquely suitable site for research only to the extent that it exerts on faculty and students alike very strong social pressure to produce, and to the extent that the degree of freedom enjoyed by investigators is greater than in other laboratories. To the extent that a university relinquishes freedom and fails to establish standards and the expectancy of excellence, it relinquishes its unique characteristics. In the long run it will lose quality, stature, and usefulness. Indeed, unless universities place the attainment and maintenance of freedom and excellence above all other goals, they will tend to lose their identity as universities, their capacity to perform the functions which justify their existence, and the privileges and immunities granted to them by society.

Only to the extent that universities are places where freedom is greater and the social pressures to produce are more intense than in other institutions are they the "natural home of basic research." Some research organizations provide a greater degree of freedom than some universities. For example, Dr. Vannevar Bush has said of the Carnegie Institution:

> Its staff is freer, in the best sense, than that of almost any other scientific group . . . It is only in certain universities, in the case of men whose position and reputation make them immune, and in a few choice spots in industry, government, and some scientific institutions that we find groups with the freedom to choose and pursue their work which is enjoyed by the staff throughout the institution.[9]

Organizations providing this degree of freedom, whether financed by endowment, government, or industry, are in every sense as "natural" a home of basic research as universities.

This emphasis upon freedom as the unique institutional contribution of universities has a direct and important implication for the attitude of universities towards federal research funds. To the extent that maintenance of freedom is a primary objective of universities, it follows that close attention should be paid to the effects of federal research funds on the freedom of faculty members and the freedom of the university as an institution. The characteristics of federal research grants and contracts that most directly affect the freedom of faculty members are the terms and conditions under which the funds are provided. These terms and conditions, discussed in Chapter 6, include stability of support, amount of "elbow room" allowed to investigators, reporting and auditing requirements, and secrecy and security measures.

Conversely, the freedom of universities is not determined primarily by the scientific substance of research financed by federal agencies. Indeed, whether the work is called "basic," "applied," or "developmental" has little to do with the freedom of universities. In short, the terms and conditions under which federal research funds are provided are more significant to the universities than is the label applied to the research.

Reconciliation of goals and functions

Universities and the federal agencies continually seek adjustments that will permit each party to get as much as possible of what it wants while sacrificing as little as possible.

Two general problems, specific aspects of which crop up in various forms, lie at the root of the problem of reconciliation.

First, the federal research funds are limited to one function of the university — the extension of knowledge. In general, the federal agencies are forced, by reason of the statutes under which they operate and through which the limits of their actions are set, to view research as separate from the conservation and diffusion of knowledge. The universities, on the other hand, must consider the three functions as intermingled and inseparable. For this reason, differences of purpose, emphasis, and point of view between universities and the federal agencies are inherent in the existing system.

Second, some federal agencies — the Department of Defense in particular — have missions of such urgency that they are impelled to view universities much as they view industrial concerns, as organizations with people and facilities which can produce results important to national defense. These federal agencies cannot view universities as institutions with unique and in-

34

dispensable functions that must, in the interest of a politically, economically, and militarily sound nation, be performed well. The zealous, single-minded drive toward the attainment of an operating objective of a federal agency — such as the rapid development of effective intermediate range and intercontinental ballistics missiles — can create points of conflict with universities. Continuing friction seems inevitable if the total effect of the actions of all federal agencies is strong pressure to change universities, against their wills, into research organizations.

The more extensive and the more permanent the interests of the federal government in research in universities, the greater should be its interest in the total health of the universities. The federal agencies can, within limits, modify their practices to increase the long-range efficiency of universities as sites for research. How and how much the agencies modify their programs for financing research in the light of nonresearch objectives of universities depends in large part on the time span over which the agencies view their research mission. In general, the longer the view of the federal agency, the more relevant do the nonresearch objectives of universities become to the research objectives of the federal agencies, and the more pertinent becomes the vigor of the university as a whole. To be more specific, a federal agency may pay attention to the effect of its research funds on the training of graduate students if the agency believes that it must depend on the current crop of graduate students to produce research a decade in the future. A federal agency will tend to be more willing to modify its rules in order to help finance the library or improve the general administration of the university if the agency believes that in the long run the university as a whole must be strong in order to serve as an effective site for purchased or supported research. If the federal agency believes that there will not be any long run if it fails to accomplish its mission — national defense, for example — it need not subordinate effective performance of its tasks to the long-range welfare of our system of higher education.

When a federal agency takes a long-range view and is therefore willing to adapt its policies to make universities more effective as research centers, some practical problems arise.

One of the most difficult problems relates to the mechanisms

35

required for effective adaptation of the policies of federal agencies to the general needs of universities. From the point of view of the individual agency, the dependence of the federal government on a strong university system for the performance of research of high quality is not clear. Moreover, the separate federal agencies have no statutory authority and in general no desire to move beyond the research mission. Only when the total effect of all federal programs for financing research is taken into account do the important effects of the federal money on the total long-run health of the universities become fully apparent. No effective mechanism has yet been developed for defining generally the extent to which and the manner in which federal agencies should take into account the vigor of universities as a factor affecting their long-range capacity to perform research of high quality.

From the point of view of universities, a fundamental problem in reconciling the objectives of the federal government and those of universities relates to how and how well universities discharge their obligations to society, not only to the federal government but to the total society of which government is a part.

The problem was recognized by some universities in the early postwar years. In discussing emerging problems at the University of California as federal research support grew after World War II, a faculty committee saw the alternative policy courses that exist for all universities. The committee said in 1950:

> The university . . . may take the position that it will limit its staff to the size necessary to carry on its teaching program, providing such research facilities as are necessary to satisfy the requirements of staff members and graduate students, assuming that staff members normally devote about half time to research. Size of staff is then determined primarily by teaching requirements, and the extent of research activity is limited accordingly . . . On the other hand, with an expanding national program of research, the research activities of the university will be extended to the extent necessary to meet public demands.[10]

The problem of reconciling the objectives of federal agencies with those of universities is perhaps most clearly seen in relation to the conduct of defense research by universities, and particularly to classified defense research.

During and after World War II the Department of Defense

exerted pressure on universities to accept defense research contracts. The university people who have fully grasped the urgency of defense research have also consistently pleaded the case for directing university resources and talents to problems of defense. That this has not been a flash reaction to highly publicized Russian accomplishments is indicated by the following passage from the Riehlman report, a 1954 congressional document on the administration of the military research and development program: "The subcommittee concurs with the views of the many witnesses who testified that one of the controlling considerations affecting the efficiency of a research and development program in a governmental agency is the urgency of the work to be done." Dr. Killian's testimony to the subcommittee on this point was particularly impressive: "I think the only way we are going to meet this problem, since it comes down to a problem of recruiting first-rate personnel for these projects, is for the Government to indicate the urgency of those projects being carried through successfully." [11]

Ex-President Dodds of Princeton also has expressed his belief that private universities should undertake defense research: "To date the government's chief interest, indeed the prime political justification for most of its research contracts with universities, is national defense. This imposes a certain responsibility upon universities to accept projects which may contribute to national safety." He then proceeded, however, to outline a deeper obligation of universities: "Universities, however, cannot afford to be swerved from their obligation to advance fundamental knowledge irrespective of measured utilitarian values. Investigation for the purposes of quick results which can promptly be put into production must always be accommodated to our historic function to seek out new knowledge for itself alone." [12]

The deeper obligation relates to the functions which universities serve for society as contrasted with those functions performed by government for society.

This question of the nature of the obligations of universities can be seen clearly when one considers whether, the extent to which, and the conditions under which universities should conduct secret research. A few universities, among them Harvard, assess the deleterious effect of secret research as being so significant that they refuse to accept any classified projects. If this policy had been followed by all universities during the postwar years, either the national security would have been endangered by failure to have the research done or competent faculty members would have been taken from universities to conduct research elsewhere. This does not mean, however, that Harvard and the other institutions which refuse classified research are endangering the national security or evading a moral responsibility. They believe that they can most effectively serve society by remaining islands of open freedom. It would be hard to argue that the maintenance of such strong centers is not of great value to the nation.

The institutional arrangements by which the objectives of universities are reconciled with those of the government are complex. In a later chapter there is described the network of university groups, nongovernment study groups and commissions, and advisory groups in federal agencies that are the primary mechanism through which this process of reconciliation is carried out. The maintenance of communication between federal agencies and universities at every level is the most important single prerequisite to reconciling the aims and needs of the government and the universities. These levels extend from the individual faculty member and the federal scientist to the representatives of universities who deal with cabinet members and their immediate staffs.

No clear and simple administrative structure and mechanism to clarify the relation of the federal government as a purchaser and sponsor of research to universities as teaching and research organizations has been devised at this time. A means for solving a problem can hardly be offered before the problem is recognized, and the fact that the continuing research effort inevitably drives the federal government to consider the total activities is still not universally admitted.

3

Federal Research Funds

Federal research funds make up a substantial part of the operating income of universities. The sheer volume of money affects what they teach, how they teach, and the quality of instruction. The balance between the conservation, transmission, and discovery of knowledge is affected. Moreover, universities are influenced not only by the federal funds which they receive, but by the total volume of federal research and development funds. For example, the federal funds have created a demand for engineering and scientific manpower which has drawn many university teachers and potential teachers into industrial research. These are not temporary effects and they will in all probability become steadily more powerful.

For reasons such as these, a general understanding of the magnitude of federal research and development expenditures is helpful to an understanding of the total effects of federal research funds on universities.

National research and development expenditures

National research and development expenditures have increased throughout this century and exceeded $10 billion* in 1958.[1] Moreover, the proportion of the gross national product — the total net volume of goods and service produced in the country during a given period — represented by research and development has been rising steadily.* From about 0.25 percent of the gross national

---

* None of the figures in this section is adjusted for price changes. Adjustment is not important when such relations as those between gross national product and

product twenty years ago, research and development expenditures have risen until they now equal somewhat more than 2 percent of the gross national product (Appendix table 1).

In all probability, research and development expenditures will continue to increase in real terms and as a proportion of the gross national product. The economy can sustain the long-term growth rate characteristic of the past decades and required for reasonably full employment in the future only through a steadily growing volume of investment. Expansion of investment is in turn dependent upon innovation and change, and these rest upon research. So, quite apart from defense requirements, total national research and development expenditures will probably continue to rise at a rate no slower than has been characteristic of the decades just past. It is reasonable to assume that the gross national product will continue to expand at a compound rate of about 3 percent a year. It is also reasonable to assume that in an increasingly technological economy, research and development expenditures will gradually expand to a level of 3 to 3.5 percent of the gross national product by 1970. These growth rates would produce a total national research and development program costing $20 to $25 billion in 1970, at 1959 prices.

About half of all research and development in this country is financed by federal agencies; even if defense research expenditures were to decline, the federal government would probably continue to finance a substantial share of the nation's research and development effort.

Research and development expenditures have been a gradually increasing proportion of the federal budget since the middle of

---

research and development expenditures, are being examined because the prices involved have risen at about the same rate. When absolute magnitudes are under consideration, however, it is well to bear in mind that prices have risen.

While no price index for research and development exists, it is reasonable to assume that these costs have risen by about the same amount as other prices. The price deflators for the gross national product can be used as a rough measure of the rise in research costs. The price deflator for the gross national product rose from 74.6 in 1946 (with 1947 as 100) to 110.7 in 1958 (*Economic Report of the President*, January 1959, Table D–5, p. 144). This is an increase of almost 50 percent. The current level of about $10 billion for research and development could have been financed for about $6.7 billion in 1946. In real terms, the nation's total research and development effort has expanded not fivefold, but by somewhat more than three times — from $2 billion to $6.7 billion.

World War II. Between 1940 and 1945, federal research and development expenditures grew from 0.8 percent to 1.6 percent of the total federal budget. In the postwar years, the figure has risen steadily from about 4 to about 7 percent of the federal budget. For the fiscal year 1960, for example, the President proposed a total federal budget of $77 billion and a research and development budget of almost $5.5 billion, about 7 percent of the total.[2]

Three major recipients

The major recipients of federal research and development funds are federal laboratories, industrial laboratories, and the laboratories of nonprofit institutions including not only colleges and universities, but also hospitals, foundations, and independent research institutes. In 1959, 15 percent of all federal research and

CHART I

DISTRIBUTION OF THE FEDERAL RESEARCH DOLLAR, 1959

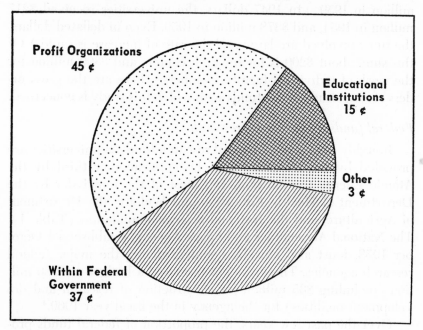

Source: Federal Funds for Science, VII, p. 10

development funds is going to educational institutions, as contrasted with 45 percent to industrial laboratories, 37 percent for work in federal laboratories and 3 percent to other institutions.

Since 1952, from 12 to 19 percent of the federal research and development funds have gone to non-profit institutions (Appendix table 2). About 80 percent of this amount has gone to educational institutions in recent years (Appendix table 3). The distinction between research and development should be made here. About two-thirds of the federal money spent in federal and industrial laboratories is for development. Virtually all of the money spent in universities is for research. While the border zone between research and development is broad, there is no doubt that the significance of universities for research — for investigation not related to making superior hardware — is much greater than is indicated by the proportion of total federal research and development funds spent in universities.[3]

In absolute terms, the funds supplied to universities have approximately doubled from $260 million in 1954 to almost $500 million in 1959. (In 1947 dollars, the universities received $217 million in 1954, and $378 million in 1959. Even in deflated dollars, the sums involved are large and the rate of increase is rapid.) Of this sum, about $200 is for research centers and $300 million for the work of individual faculty members. These are the gross orders of magnitude of the funds with which this study is concerned.

Federal funds for university research

Roughly a third of all federal research funds in universities are provided by the Department of Defense, another third by the Atomic Energy Commission, and most of the remainder by the Department of Health, Education and Welfare, the Department of Agriculture, and the National Science Foundation (Table 1). The National Aeronautics and Space Agency, established 1 October 1958, must also now be counted among the major federal research agencies. The President proposed a budget of $280 million (including $35 million for construction of research and development facilities) for the agency in the fiscal year 1960.[4]

Over the past few years, the proportion of federal funds provided by the Department of Defense to universities has declined

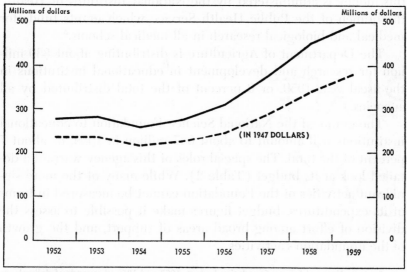

CHART II

FEDERAL RESEARCH FUNDS TO UNIVERSITIES RISING

Source: Appendix Table 3
Economic Report of the President, 1958.
(Prices deflated by the deflator used for the gross National Product)

Table 1. Federal research and development funds to educational institutions,
by administering agency, 1959 (millions of dollars)

Agency	All universities		Research centers	
	Amount	Percent	Amount	Percent
Total	497	100	200	100
Department of Defense	179 a	36	70	35
Air Force	(54)	(11)	(11)	(6)
Navy	(62)	(12)	(18)	(9)
Army	(63)	(13)	(41)	(20)
Atomic Energy Commission	167	34	130	65
Department of Health, Education and Welfare	79	16	0	0
Department of Agriculture	30	6	0	0
National Science Foundation	37	7	0	0
Other Agencies	5	1	0	0

Source: National Science Foundation, *Federal Funds for Science*, vol. 7, pp. 72–74.
a $10,000,000 in departmentwide funds distributed among the services in proportion to their expenditure in educational institutions.

steadily, the share of the Atomic Energy Commission has remained about constant, and the part provided by other civilian agencies has risen from about a fifth to a third.

43

About 16 percent of the funds are administered by the Department of Health, Education and Welfare. More than 90 percent of this money is administered by the National Institutes of Health, the branch of the Public Health Service which grants funds for medical and biological research in all medical schools.[5]

The Department of Agriculture is distributing about $30 million for research and development in educational institutions in the fiscal year 1959, or 6 percent of the total distributed by all agencies.

The grants of the National Science Foundation to educational institutions will amount to about $37 million in 1959, or about 7 percent of the total. The special roles of this agency warrant a detailed look at its budget (Table 2). While many of the more significant activities of the Foundation cannot be measured in terms of its expenditures, budget figures make it possible to assess the division of effort among broad areas of support, and the growth of the Foundation's activities.

Table 2. National Science Foundation budget, 1952 and 1959 (thousands of dollars)

Category	1952 Amount	1952 Percent	1959 Amount	1959 Percent
Total	3,500	100	140,000	100
National science policy studies	130	4	1,700	1
Research grants	1,074	30	45,800	33
Research facilities	0	0	9,300	7
Fellowships	1,533	44	3,200	2
Science education	7	0	78,600	56
Other [a]	756	22	1,400	1

[a] Includes review of research and training programs, dissemination of scientific information, attendance at international meetings, assistance to other federal scientific activities, and executive direction and management.

From the first significant appropriation of $3.5 million in the fiscal year 1952, the appropriation grew to $50 million in the fiscal years 1957 and 1958. For the fiscal year 1959, the President's budget proposed an appropriation of $140 million. The increases were proposed to support more research, to disseminate research findings more effectively and, in the words of the President's budget, "particularly for increased emphasis on programs to improve science teaching and to increase the number of highly qualified research scientists in this country." Practically all of the funds, except for those allotted to a large program for training secondary-school science teachers are made available to university faculty members or students, or to universities themselves.

The salient characteristics of the evolution of the budget of the Foundation, apart from steady growth, and a sharp increase from $50 million in 1958 to $140 million in 1959, have been these:

(1) Rapid expansion of national science policy studies from 1952 through 1955, with slower growth in later years.

(2) Marked and uninterrupted increase in funds for research grants.

(3) Steady but moderate growth of research fellowship funds.

(4) A phenomenal expansion of funds for education in the sciences, beginning in 1957, prompted primarily by public concern over Russian accomplishments in education.

(5) Initiation in 1956 of a program to provide large facilities for basic research, primarily in the mathematical, physical, and engineering sciences.

The heavy emphasis within the Foundation on the education function, and the large proportion of the Foundation's budget consistently devoted to this function, are less widely known than its research support function.

The remaining $4 million distributed by federal agencies to educational institutions, accounting for 1 percent of the total, was administered by thirteen federal agencies (Table A–4).

From the points of view of both the administering agency and the recipient of federal research funds, the proportion of the funds of each agency which goes to colleges and universities is significant. In research, as in other functional areas of federal activity general attitudes and administrative practices are in large part determined by the kinds of institutions and people with whom business is conducted. Only 7 percent of the research and development expenditures of the Department of Defense and 27 percent of the Atomic Energy Commission research funds are for research contracts with educational institutions; whereas, 83 percent of the funds of the National Science Foundation and 46 percent of the funds of the Department of Health, Education and Welfare go to educational institutions.

It is important to distinguish between the $300 million supplied to faculty members in university departments and the $200 million (Table 1) supplied by the Department of Defense (about $80 million) and the Atomic Energy Commission (about $120 million) to large research centers. As will be shown in Chapter 10, the questions of policy and operations arising from the development of these centers are for the most part quite different from the problems created by research grants or contracts for the research of faculty members.

The volume of federal funds for the work of individual faculty members has risen markedly from $136 million to $296 million over the period from 1952 to 1959 (Table 3). The rise has been particularly marked over the period 1956–1958. With this increase

Table 3. Federal funds for support of the research of individual faculty members, excluding research centers, 1952 and 1959 (millions of dollars)

Agency	1952	1959	Change
Total	136	296	+160
Department of Defense	100	108	+ 8
Atomic Energy Commission	3	37	+ 34
Department of Health, Education and Welfare	14	79	+ 65
Department of Agriculture	13	30	+ 17
National Science Foundation	1	38	+ 37
All other agencies	5	4	− 1

Source: Table A-5.

in total support, there have been some marked shifts in the sources of these funds. Department of Defense research contracts rose by only $8 million over the period 1952–1958, and they declined from 73 percent to 36 percent of all federal funds provided to individual faculty members. On the other hand, Atomic Energy Commission contracts increased by $32 million and those of other agencies by $112 million.

In short, federal funds for the work of individual faculty members have in recent years not only increased steadily but have been provided to an increasing degree by agencies other than the Department of Defense and the Atomic Energy Commission (Table A–5).

46

CHART III

THE FEDERAL RESEARCH DOLLAR FOR UNIVERSITY RESEARCH
- Support more diversified
- Share of Defense Declining

Funds for individual faculty members :

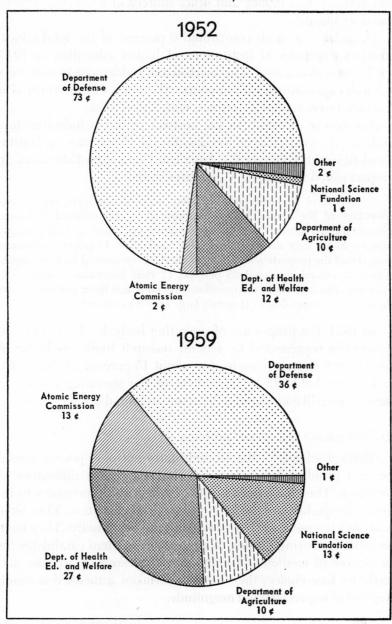

1952

Department
of Defense
73 ¢

Other
2 ¢

National Science
Fundation
1 ¢

Department of
Agriculture
10 ¢

Atomic Energy
Commission
2 ¢

Dept. of Health
Ed. and Welfare
12 ¢

1959

Department
of Defense
36 ¢

Atomic Energy
Commission
13 ¢

Other
1 ¢

National Science
Fundation
13 ¢

Dept. of Health
Ed. and Welfare
27 ¢

Department of
Agriculture
10 ¢

Source : Appendix Tables 3 and 5

Federal funds and university income

Not only the absolute volume of federal funds, but the relation between this money and other sources of university income also is significant.

Organized research constituted 6 percent of the total educational expenditures of institutions of higher education in 1940, but 14 percent in 1950.[6] This marked and sudden rise in university research expenditures was, of course, the result of the World War II armed forces research contracts with universities.

The course of events in the postwar period is indicated in a study for the year 1952 undertaken for the Committee on Institutional Research Policy of the American Council on Education. In a report issued in 1954, the Committee stated:

> Of a total of 30 institutions reporting regarding budgets, the average percentage of the annual budget represented by Government sponsored research was 16 percent . . . In a comparison of private and state institutions, we find a large discrepancy. In this breakdown, 13 private institutions showed that the proportion of the annual budget represented by Government sponsored research averaged 25 percent; 17 state institutions showed only 8 percent. The answers to the questionnaire, on which these percentages are based, exclude expenditures at certain large research centers.[7]

In 1954, the proportion of operating budgets of colleges and universities represented by federal research funds, exclusive of the research centers, remained at about 15 percent (Table A–6). In 1959, probably 15 to 20 percent of the operating income of universities will come from federal research funds.

Medical schools — a special problem

Medical schools in the United States not only pose a special financial problem for universities, but they have difficulties of their own. They have been pushed by irresistible pressures to increase the quality and the length of medical education. They have expanded the services they provide to the community. They have borne an increasing burden of students other than candidates for the degree of medicine. Finally, partly because of pressure and partly by free choice, they have undertaken a medical research program of unprecedented magnitude.

Medical education imposes a heavy financial drain on universities. The latest comprehensive study of the finances of medical schools in relation to university finance, J. D. Millett's *Financing Higher Education in the United States*, shows that in both public and private universities which have medical schools, medical expenditures were 20 percent or more of total institutional expenditures, but medical degrees were only 5 percent of all degrees. Millett concludes that "medical education is one of the most costly programs of higher education" and that "medical education is of major financial concern for most universities with a medical school."

As with many other aspects of the financing of research in universities, the prewar and postwar pictures contrast sharply. For example, research expenditures in tax-supported medical schools increased from 9 percent of total medical school expenditures in 1941 to 25 percent in 1951 (Table 4). The comparable

Table 4. Percentage distribution of medical school expenditures and income, 1941 and 1951

	22 tax-supported schools		37 private schools	
Distribution	1941	1951	1941	1951
Activity	*Expenditures*			
Total	100	100	100	100
Instruction	56	52	59	40
Research	9	25	13	38
Administration	9	7	10	9
Maintenance	11	10	8	7
Other [a]	15	6	10	6
Source	*Income*			
Total	100	100	100	100
Tuition	20	10	35	20
Taxes	49	70	3	30
Private gifts	11	13	21	23
Endowment and other	20	7	41	27

Source: J. E. Deitrick and R. C. Berson, *Medical Schools in the United States at Midcentury* (New York: McGraw-Hill, 1953), pp. 89–97.
[a] Excludes hospitals and clinics; includes libraries, separately organized postgraduate education, and student health services.

figures for private schools were 13 and 38 percent. The increase in the proportion of expenditures for research has been accompanied by a decline in the proportion of expenditures for instruction — from 59 percent to 40 percent in the case of private schools.

The shift in the patterns of expenditure was accompanied by an even larger shift in sources of income. Taxes rose sharply as a source of income over the period 1941–1951 from 49 to 70 percent for tax-supported schools. Even among the private schools taxes provided 30 percent of income in 1951 as contrasted with 3 percent in 1941. Most of the increase in tax funds is accounted for by federal research grant and contract funds. By 1951 tuition had declined to 10 percent of the income of the public schools and 20 percent of the income of the private schools. Endowment income had declined to 7 and 27 percent, respectively, of the income of the public and private schools.

While the most dramatic changes in the patterns of expenditure and income of medical schools came about over the decade 1941–1951, the trends established during that period have continued. Tuition continues to decline in importance as a source of income, and now represents only 12 percent of income (Table 5).

Table 5. Income of medical schools, 1956–57 (millions of dollars)

Source	Amount	Percent
Grand total	178.7	100
Subtotal exclusive of outside sources	111.2	62
Government appropriations	52.7	29
General university funds	7.5	4
Medical school endowment	12.8	8
Tuition	20.3	12
Gifts	8.3	4
Other	9.6	5
Subtotal of outside sources		38
Research	58.4	33
Teaching	9.1	5

Source: "Medical Education in the United States and Canada," *Journal of the American Medical Association* 161, 1645 (1956).

The combined income provided by general university funds and medical school endowments accounts for only another 12 percent of medical school income. On the other hand, research funds from outside sources — mostly federal funds — account for a third of the total income of medical schools. The schools are depending more and more on outside sources of funds, and the teaching function is meagerly financed as compared with the research function.

It is clear that if medical schools undertake research with federal funds supplied under conditions which do not cover the full cost of the research, the financial plight of the schools and of the parent universities will become even more serious. University and medical school officials have, therefore, expressed great concern over the fact that the National Institutes of Health have not paid all of the indirect costs of research which they support.

On broader grounds, the extreme financial difficulties faced by medical schools bring into sharp focus the nature of the relation between teaching and research in universities, and the relations between federal support for research, construction, and operating expenses. Unless money for the general support of medical education forthcoming from private sources is multiplied several times over in the near future, the result will be either a dangerous decline in the quality of medical education or a program of general federal support for the medical school.

Federal financing by field

More than 70 percent of all research conducted by universities is financed by the federal government (Table A–7). This proportion varies from more than 90 percent in physics and mathematics to 25 percent in the social sciences.[8] In the life sciences, the government provides about half of the university research budget. In no field of science does the government finance less than a quarter of the separately budgeted research carried on in universities.

Universities themselves finance less than 10 percent of all the research they conduct. All of the remainder comes from federal sources and other sources outside the universities. In the physical sciences, university funds have practically disappeared as a source of support. Universities finance less than a quarter of all faculty research in the social sciences, the field in which the proportion of university support is highest.

There is some tendency for nonfederal funds to be concentrated in fields where the federal financing is relatively light (Table 6).

Both foundations and industry provide larger sums for university research than the universities themselves (Table A–8).

51

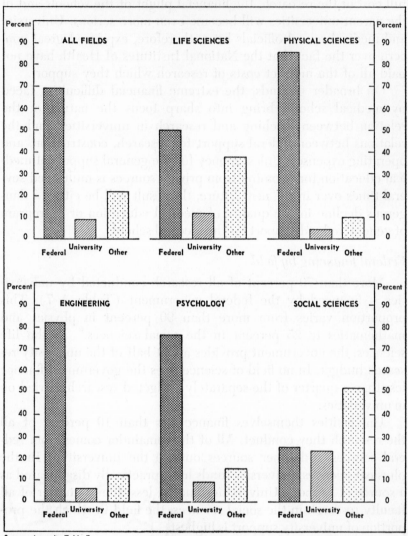

CHART IV

FEDERAL SUPPORT OF UNIVERSITY RESEARCH, BY FIELD

Source: Appendix Table 7

Industrial grants and contracts finance more than three times as much university research in chemistry and more than twice as much engineering research as is financed from university funds.

Foundations pay for more research in the social sciences than is financed from university sources.

Table 6. Percentage distribution of sources of research funds, by field

Field	Total	Federal	Foundation	University
All fields	100	100	100	100
Engineering	31	37	2	20
Physical sciences	27	33	6	15
Life sciences	32	24	70	43
Psychology	3	3	3	3
Social sciences	6	2	18	17
Arts and humanities	1	1	1	2

Source: Table A-7.

Policy problems inherent in federal financing of research in public and private institutions of higher learning do not lie wholly in the future. The trustees of the Carnegie Foundation for the Advancement of Teaching have stated the situation forcefully and accurately:

The use of federal funds in higher education is often discussed as though it did not occur at present but were a question for the future . . . This is grossly misleading. Federal funds are flowing to the universities in exceedingly impressive amounts, and no one involved — federal agencies, college presidents, trustees, or faculty members — shows any concerted inclination to stop the flow. It is very difficult to find educational leaders who are willing to predict that the channeling of federal funds to higher education will decrease in the foreseeable future. Many predict an inevitable *increase*.

In short, the question at issue is not whether the federal government should have a role in higher education. That question was settled affirmatively in the nineteenth century and never seriously reopened. The question at issue is *what kind* of role the federal government should play in higher education.[9]

One central issue in the remainder of this book is whether it is possible to have strong, free, productive research in the university structure when most of the money comes from the federal government. The sheer volume of funds, apart from the distribution among fields of science or between basic and applied research, creates pressures of the utmost importance in universities. If the financing of a large proportion of university research from outside sources, and particularly from the government, will lead to loss of freedom by universities and by investigators, the universities

53

and the scientific community are in an extremely precarious position.

Institutional and geographic distribution

The government has no general policy with respect to the distribution of research grants and contracts. Each agency decides what it wants to do within broad areas defined by statute. In general, federal agencies which purchase research simply seek out places where it can be done most effectively and rapidly. Agencies which support research, such as the Office of Naval Research, the National Science Foundation, and the National Institutes of Health, have a more complex problem. Ideally, those who support a field of research are interested in promoting the long-run health of the field. They ought therefore, for example, to avoid a highly centralized scientific structure in which competition among schools of thought may be stifled. At the same time, they must on both scientific and political grounds undertake to support the investigators currently able to do research of high quality.

Whatever the objectives of the federal agencies are, their actions have resulted in heavy concentrations of funds in a few universities. In 1950, the following 17 universities (12 private and 5 state) received the largest volume of federal research grants and contracts awarded to universities, excluding funds for the operation of research centers: The California Institute of Technology, The University of Chicago, Columbia University, Cornell University, Harvard University, The Illinois Institute of Technology, The Johns Hopkins University, The Massachusetts Institute of Technology, The University of Pennsylvania, Princeton University, The University of Rochester, Stanford University, The University of California, The University of Illinois, Iowa State College, The University of Michigan, and The University of Minnesota.

In 1953–54, 14 universities of the 173 receiving any funds received 55 percent of all Federal research funds supplied to universities, excluding funds supplied to research centers (Table A–9). Since the federal administrators have actively sought out research talent and facilities, one may infer that only 175 to 200 of the nation's 1,500 institutions of higher education have the capacity for significant research undertakings.

Concentration of funds in a few universities continues to characterize the distribution of funds by each of the major federal agencies. In general, the Department of Defense and the Atomic Energy Commission concentrate their funds somewhat more heavily than the National Science Foundation and the Department of Health, Education and Welfare. Even so, ten universities receive about a third of the grant funds of the National Science Foundation and of the Public Health Service.[10] Seven universities of the ten — California, Harvard, Chicago, Yale, Columbia, Pennsylvania, and Johns Hopkins — receive the largest sums from each of the two agencies. Of ten recipients of the largest volume of Public Health Service grants in 1951 and 1959, California, Harvard, Columbia, Minnesota, Johns Hopkins, New York University, Pennsylvania, and Chicago are on both lists.

Industrial and foundation support also is highly concentrated — and concentrated in the same universities which receive the bulk of the federal research money. For example, 13 of the 138 universities receiving foundation money account for 55 percent of the total foundation research support.[11] Not only does private support of research exert no force for dispersion to counteract the concentration of federal support, but the patterns of public and private support reinforce each other in sustaining or increasing the degree of concentration.

Federal research funds are highly concentrated in a few universities because the university structure of the nation has a highly concentrated research capacity. One of the best measures of research capacity is the production of doctors of philosophy. In 1954–55, five universities granted 24 percent of all Ph.D.'s in science.[12] The concentration of science doctorates and of federal research funds is highly correlated. Thus, the National Science Foundation found that in 1952 the 25 institutions (excluding research centers) receiving 66 percent of the federal research grant and contract funds awarded 69 percent of the science doctorates.[13]

In summary, the federal agencies have put money where research capacity has been demonstrated. The funds have not been used to a significant extent as an instrument to strengthen universities with weak research potential. The agencies have not, with the exception of the Department of Agriculture, distributed funds with an eye to geographical spread.

Why has the Department of Agriculture been the only federal agency to establish deliberately a geographically diversified research structure? Three primary forces seem responsible. First, because of wide geographical variations in the physical factors affecting plants and animals — soil, water, and climate — much of the research must be done where the local problems are found. Second, farmers as a clientele group have insisted that research be practical, that it be conducted locally, and that the results be made available to them. Third, there is a strong tradition of operation of federal agricultural programs through states, soil conservation districts, and other local groups.

The unique characteristics of the Department of Agriculture's research program become clear when contrasted with those of the Atomic Energy Commission, the Department of Defense, the National Advisory Committee on Aeronautics, the National Science Foundation, and the Public Health Service. The clientele pressures, the fundamental significance of local natural conditions for the substance of research, and the strong tradition of operating with state agencies are either entirely absent or much less influential in determining geographic distribution of research for these agencies. Indeed, departure from the federal-regional-state-local pattern of operation, which in itself exerts a strong force toward wide geographic distribution of funds, has been a fundamental aspect of the federal research structure both during and after World War II.

This administrative innovation has created stress in some federal agencies, such as the Public Health Service, which have traditionally discharged the bulk of their operating responsibilities through or with the cooperation of state governments. A new network of administrative and political relations for research support has been superimposed upon the standard operating relations. The research organizations undertake to avoid the older federal-state channels in order to deal directly with those in universities and other research organizations who have similar professional interests and who are powerful allies.

56

There remains the set of research centers and their relation to the question of concentration of research. The development of the centers demonstrated conclusively that major research organizations can be created rapidly in association with universities. The centers, created *de novo* on a large scale, could have served as the instrument for geographic distribution of the nation's research structure. They could not, however, have served as a means of diversifying the institutional distribution of funds because only large universities could manage the large centers associated with universities. Considerations other than geographic distribution of research governed their location. The centers were set up to perform urgent tasks, defined in broad terms, for the Department of Defense and the Atomic Energy Commission. The effective performance of these tasks properly took precedence over all other considerations when the centers were set up.

The result has been a geographic distribution of funds which mirrors the institutional concentration of research talent and facilities. Regional or state distribution of funds relates to nothing common to the states in the region or peculiar to geographical or political regions as a whole. The geographical distribution of federal research funds — with the exception of the agricultural funds — is nothing but a reflection of the size and type of research organization found in the states of the region.

Given these facts with respect to the high concentration of federal research funds, what conclusions may be drawn?

A more widely diversified research structure would be desirable in this country. The existing degree of concentration is greater than is required by the nature of the physical facilities involved, the nature of problems to be solved, or the optimum concentration of talent for a university of very high quality. Large aggregations of people and equipment are required for modern research, but not so large as those found at the largest universities.

An increase in the scale of research at many universities where research is now pursued on a small scale would be sound for a number of reasons. If research is necessary to good teaching, then a concentration of federal research funds which limits support to a small proportion of universities may keep the others from de-

57

veloping as strong centers of learning and cause a decline in the quality of faculty and graduate students.

A high concentration of research brings with it the possibility that the general views and philosophy of a few large universities will have too influential a voice in shaping public policy. One unfortunate consequence of this concentration could be acceptance of the doctrine that a few outstanding institutions are destined to be intellectual leaders and that others are to be the custodians of mediocrity. President Du Bridge, of the California Institute of Technology, has expressed his belief that:

Colleges and universities should face more frankly the range of intellectual caliber to be found among their students and the level to which each institution wishes to cater.

At present no college dares to admit — even to itself — that it is going to cater to the middle or lower third of college students rather than the upper third . . . Some colleges have to hit the bottom of the barrel, particularly the state institutions that are required by law to admit all applicants with high school diplomas . . . I think it is important that a few institutions or schools of science and engineering be encouraged to devote their resources to the sole task of improving quality without trying to grow in size.[14]

There can certainly be no argument against emphasizing quality of training. One can, however, question whether abandonment of the ideal of excellence by all but a few institutions of higher education would be in the national interest. Certainly strength lies in the multiplication of places where excellence can be and is fostered.

A related potential danger is that of scientific orthodoxy and of the dominance of schools of thought, made possible by great concentrations of intellectual leaders, research workers, and funds. I do not believe, however, that this danger is to be taken seriously.

Even if it is admitted that federal research funds are overconcentrated, it does not necessarily follow that the policies of federal agencies should be changed. Research in this country is not above the ideological fight pervading our education system since colonial days. The argument is over definitions of democracy. One school of thought holds that the national welfare is best served by encouraging types of training designed to foster the fullest development of the few intellects at the upper end of the intelligence scale. Access to training would be open to all students who could meet stiff requirements, and denied to none except on the basis of intellectual inability. The opposing school of thought holds this would be undemocratic in principle — that in the long run it would endanger the national welfare by creating an intellectual aristocracy.

The present danger is not the creation of an intellectual elite but rather the strong forces pushing toward conformity, toward "life adjustment," toward the average as the ideal. For this reason, the tendency of the federal agencies to make the capacity of the investigator the primary criterion in distributing research funds is sound. It is a force opposing distribution of money on bases other than excellence.

While I think it desirable for the federal government to promote more aggressively the growth of research in a large number of universities, through deliberate use of the existing research grant and contract mechanisms, I have some reservations as to the effectiveness of such a policy,

First, strong university research cannot, in contrast with the research centers, be built by research funds alone. Enough local funds must be available to permit the faculty to carry a relatively light teaching load. There must be a strong nucleus of capable investigators in one or more fields. The administration of the university must understand and foster the conditions under which research of high quality will prosper. In short, a strong research program can exist in a university only if the total environment is favorable, and research funds can provide only parts of that environment.

Moreover, a decision to establish a strong research center deliberately changes an existing educational pattern. All universities cannot be strengthened simultaneously if for no other reason than that the number of capable people is limited. This means that choices must be made among colleges and universities. This is inevitably a political matter outside the politics of science. The problem would be best dealt with by groups not composed exclusively of research-oriented agencies, administrators, and advisers.

Finally, as was pointed out earlier, the federal structure for financing research does not permit review of the needs of universities as functioning organizations. Even if all federal agencies attempted to strengthen research in universities where the present effort is relatively weak, the existing administrative structure would almost certainly hamper the attempt.

If there are to be substantial changes in the distribution of research capacity among the universities of this country, the approach must be on a more fundamental level than provision of research funds to individuals who are not particularly well qualified. Large sums of public or private money must be made available to create colleges and universities strong in every respect, led by persons who will not compromise with mediocrity, staffed by faculty members of high quality with good salaries as well as time and money for research, equipped with the necessary physical facilities, sought out by the best graduate students, and totally dedicated to excellence.

4

Scientific Fields – Money and Manpower

Over the years since World War II, concern over the effect of federal research funds on the distribution of research effort by broad field has often been expressed. Many questions have been raised: Do federal funds in effect direct science by strongly influencing the volume of money and people available for various fields? Are the social sciences and social scientists neglected as a result of the concentration of federal research funds in the life sciences and the physical sciences?

This chapter is concerned with such questions, dealing with the distribution of effort first in terms of money and then in terms of manpower. But before turning to the substance of the discussion, an underlying problem must be dealt with: What are the meanings and uses of classifications of research expenditures by scientific field?

The classification problem — by field

People are complicated, and scientists are no exception. A classification of their thought processes, their experimental procedures, or even their findings according to any single scheme is almost certain to be misleading. For this reason, the significance of various distributions of research expenditures by field is sometimes misleading. The most productive function of such analyses is to provide a general overview of relatively broad fields, preferably over a span of years. It is possible to draw meaningful conclusions, for example, as to the distribution of efforts among the physical, the biological, and the social sciences. Even within a field such as medical research a general notion of the manner in which research resources are deployed between areas of study — for example, chronic diseases as compared with communicable diseases — can be provided with an adequate degree of accuracy. Precision is not required in such estimates because their proper use is in detecting broad trends. They are of value of those who are in a position to add sound judgment to the facts and to exert influence on the general distribution of research resources.

Conversely, analyses purporting to indicate the distribution of manpower or funds by fine subdivisions of scientific fields are inherently misleading. The more detailed such classifications, the greater the appearance of precision. However, such fine classification forces the work of individuals, or that part of their work financed by a research grant or contract, to be wholly allocated to one narrow scientific category. This process forces an oversimplification of what is almost invariably a complicated process which uses the approaches and techniques of a number of fields of science. When the work is jammed into some narrow specialty to secure a refined accounting of the division of effort by field, some partial aspect of the investigation must be arbitrarily selected to characterize the whole. The degree of necessary arbitrariness is so great that figures given for the funds allocated to any highly specialized field of science vary widely when different people, equally capable and equally objective, classify the research. The difficult cannot be resolved by saying that the exercise of professional judgments by highly competent people will provide the best classification. The inherent arbitrariness is such that there is no "best" classification, and people with equally good knowledge and judgment will arrive at widely different results.

Not only are these fine distributions of expenditures less exact than they appear, but they have little functional use. They are of little or no value to those who are in a position to view broad fields of science and to affect the allocation of resources. On the other hand, the scientists who know limited, specialized fields already know the situation and the competent people. This is a much better guide to decision than a detailed tabulation.

Those who do not understand the nature and limits of such fine distributions of research expenditures sometimes assume that they will be more enlightening than they are and that knowledge of the state of affairs in a specialized field of science can be advanced by statistical analyses. So far as research administrators are concerned, the primary value of such tabulations is to provide information in symbolic form to satisfy those who are not competent in any field of science but who have an exaggerated faith in statistics, or to buttress judgments reached on the basis of other factors.

With this understanding of the limits of classification of research by field, the broad distribution of university research effort, as measured by the imperfect common denominator of dollars, can be presented.[1] The overwhelming fact is that in recent years about 90 percent of all research in universities has been, as measured by dollars, in the life and physical sciences and engineering (Table 6). About 95 percent of the federal funds are for work in these three fields. Given the obvious problems of our society and our economy, including our roles in the affairs of the world, such a distribution of effort gives one pause. The universities try to redress the balance by providing 22 percent of their own research funds for investigations outside the life and physical sciences and engineering.

While these distributions of university research effort and of federal research funds by field provide an adequately precise picture, they do not indicate to what extent, if at all, the distribution of university research effort is determined by federal funds. To measure the effects of federal funds, it would first be necessary to know how the distribution of funds has shifted over the years. Such data are not available. Even if detailed statistics were available, however, it would be very difficult to do more than guess at the effects of the federal funds on the distribution of effort by field.

For one thing, developments in science as well as the availability of funds affect the distribution, and the effects of the two cannot be clearly separated. Moreover, the expenditure of money by field of science is a partial and imperfect measure of the nature and caliber of scientific effort. Finally, it is not possible to tell what would have happened to support for various fields of science if the federal funds had not been available. After all, the fields now most heavily emphasized have always been the fields in which research is most expensive and the fields which have attracted the bulk of outside funds.

Nevertheless, federal financing of university research in the life sciences, physical sciences, and engineering has been so extensive and so sustained that these fields probably represent a somewhat larger proportion of total university research programs than would have been the case if the federal funds had not been available.

Basic and applied research

There are no satisfactory measures of the amount of basic research conducted in the United States, or elsewhere for that matter. The primary cause of this situation is the fact that basic research has not been defined in objective and unambiguous terms.[2] The problem of securing an adequate definition of basic research is clearly stated in a recent report of the National Science Foundation:

> University officials estimate that, during the academic year 1953–1954, academic departments of colleges and universities and agricultural experiment stations received about $85 million for basic research from the Federal government. But Federal officials estimate that they provided barely half that amount to universities for the same purpose and during the same period.[3]

Somewhere between the offices in Washington which hand out research funds and answer questionnaires and the offices in universities which receive funds and answer questionnaires, the meaning of the definitions of basic research undergoes a metamorphosis that permits one set of observers to measure the same quantity as being twice as large as the other observers say it is. Because of this discrepancy, no statistics on the dollar value of basic research are presented here.

Such a discrepancy raises a number of questions, including the nature of the definitions that provide so flexible a measure.

Some "definitions" of basic research relate to the motive, or intent, or working conditions of the investigation. One of these is the definition of basic research given to both federal agencies and universities by the National Science Foundation as a guide to classification of research:

Basic research is that type of research directed towards increase of knowledge in science. It is research where the primary aim of the investigator is a fuller knowledge or understanding of the subject under study, rather than a practical application thereof.[4]

Another set of definitions has nothing to do with the investigator but rests on the generality, breadth, or significance of findings. This way of classifying research as basic has been well summarized by I. B. Cohen:

We thus naturally classify scientific work according to *the degree whereby it affects scientific thought and procedures;* according to *the amount by which it changes the foundation or structure of science itself.* We may well call this the fundamental character of the research. Some work is of a more fundamental character than other work simply because it exerts a greater effect on the existing structure of science, because it affects a broader area, or because within its narrow area of applicability it has a deep and penetrating effect.[5]

To reconcile the two kinds of definitions of basic research in a way that is not only logical but operationally useful, it seems to me imperative to begin by drawing a distinction, pointed out by others, which appears at first to be overly nice. "Basic findings" are fundamentally different from "basic research" because findings are an end product and research is a process. This distinction, seen clearly by Brues,[6] is not always drawn even though it is of central importance to a clear resolution of the problem of definition. Failure to draw the distinction generally leads to confusion. This is illustrated by Cohen's statement above. The system of classification implied by his definition is ambiguous because one cannot tell whether the "work" referred to is the process of research, or the findings. Literally, this "work" is a process, but the sense of the word "work" in the context of Cohen's description is "findings."

For the administrator, definitions in terms of the end product — basic science or basic findings — are not usable because decisions must be made before the research is completed and the findings are known. Administrators are forced to be prophets. They must support basic research before the returns are in. Relatively accurate predictions can be made, however, by observing the kinds of people, the kinds of motives, and the kinds of working conditions that have in the past tended to produce basic findings.

The array of criteria used to describe the research process must then be viewed not as literal descriptive definitions, but as statements of the probability of producing a basic finding. Thus, a "definition" of basic research in terms of the investigator's freedom is simply the statement of an assumption that those whose thought is not restricted and narrowly channeled are more likely to come forth with scientific ideas of great breadth or depth than those working with less freedom. Definitions in terms of the motive and intent of the investigator are essentially statements of a belief that those with wide-ranging native curiosity are more likely than others to produce basic findings.

A definition of basic research in terms of the probability that certain circumstances will lead to ideas of great scope or depth is inherently unsuitable for the purpose of collecting statistics. Not only are the circumstances too numerous, for they must include motives, working conditions, and prospective applicability of findings; but the importance to be placed on each can only be decided by the exercise of subjective judgment.

Nor can motives, attitudes, and working conditions be measured precisely. How curious must a scientist be about fundamental phenomena before his work is viewed as basic research? How remote from application must his findings be before his research is considered basic?

The criteria to be used in defining basic research and the weight to be given to each are affected by institutional goals and traditions, and personal experience and expectations. This explains why people in universities have looked at a given amount of research and decided that the proportion of this research belonging in the basic category is twice as large as the proportion placed there by federal administrators. Similar behavior is seen when engineers and physicists are asked to classify each other's work as basic or applied; less engineering and more physics are called basic than is the case when each discipline classifies its own fields.

66

Although efforts to secure adequately precise and comparable statistics by undertaking to improve the definition of basic research are futile, it is probably wise to collect and publish data on dollar expenditures for basic research in the United States. What appear to be insuperable problems of definition may prove not to be. Moreover, the nation would be better off if greater attention were paid to basic research. If our strong national predilection to rely upon statistics in reaching judgments helps to convince people of the validity of this idea, it may be worth while collecting and publishing the information even though the statistics are inherently allegorical.

Those who make decisions on the support of research use a probability approach in their day-to-day work. In practice, administrators do not decide to support work because it is basic or not basic. Indeed, the term "basic research" is used much less frequently in the day-to-day business of research administration than it is in communicating with the nonscientific world.

Administrators consider the man — his past performance as judged by his peers — even though the merit of the research project is ostensibly the basis for judgment. They consider the facilities available to him. They take into account the support available in his field — whether it is a "gap area" or one which is well financed. Those who make decisions cannot and do not attempt to judge the intentions and the motives of investigators. Definitions of basic research in terms of motive and intent are used neither in administering research nor in collecting statistics on research.

The criterion of freedom of the investigator as a condition conducive to the production of basic findings is also usable and used as a guide to research administration. More broadly, this criterion encompasses the total array of factors conducive to scientific research of high quality. H. A. Shepard, in an article in the *Journal of the Philosophy of Science* came to this conclusion:

> Efforts to define basic research operationally are . . . misleading and bring about neglect of the forces that produce it — the training, discipline, values, way of life and system of social control that motivate men to advance knowledge 'for its own sake' . . . Support for basic research means support of a social system which so motivates men.[7]

67

I suggest first, that it is impossible to define basic research operationally. Second, I think that basic research can be effectively promoted by providing funds under terms and conditions designed to strengthen the forces, values, and social system which appear as a matter of probability to promote the acquisition of knowledge.

The social sciences, arts, and humanities

The strengthening of teaching and research in fields other than the physical and biological sciences is vitally important to the national welfare. Overemphasis on the physical and biological sciences may produce intellectual distortion, a tendency to overvalue the practical and the precisely measurable, and a disinclination to reexamine fundamental values and ideas. I place the social sciences with the arts and humanities, not because the social sciences are "unscientific," but because they relate to man in nonbiological terms and to man as a social animal.

In this connection, the high concentration of federal research funds in the physical and life sciences and engineering raises questions bearing upon the past as well as upon the future. Looking backward, has the persisting pattern of federal support caused a relative neglect of research in the arts, social sciences, and humanities? Looking forward, would it be in the national interest to provide more federal funds for such research?

University research in the social sciences and humanities is now better supported than at any time in the past. About $14 million a year is now spent for research in these fields (Table A–7). Of this total, the federal government supplies about $4 million. While, as pointed out above, this $4 million is only 4 percent of total federal research expenditures in universities, in absolute terms the sum is large.

Universities provide less than the federal government for research in the social sciences — $3.4 million as against $4 million. In all probability, the university contribution would be even smaller if it were not for heavy federal contributions to the physical and life sciences and engineering.

Many institutions have a research fund derived from miscellaneous sources and administered by the dean of graduate students, a graduate council, or a special faculty research committee. Compared with federal research grants and contracts, these funds are not large. For example, $30,000 a year is the size of the fund at the University of Wisconsin and the University of Minnesota; $130,000 a year is available at the University of Illinois. For several reasons, however, these funds are more valuable than one would assume from their size. The university is free to use the money to achieve a distribution of research support that is closer to the wishes of the faculty; the funds are quickly available and can be spent with little red tape. While the average grant is fairly small, exploratory work in any field may be financed; scholarly work in the arts and humanities that would otherwise languish is aided. This support, free of all strings and all commitments, is generally considered by faculty members to be the most valuable form of assistance — dollar for dollar — available for the support of research.

Heavy concentration of federal funds in the physical and life sciences has made it possible to use larger amounts of these university research funds for the support of studies in the social sciences, arts, and humanities.

Foundations supply $4.2 million annually for research in the social sciences and humanities — more than either the federal government or universities (Table A–8). As with university funds, many foundations have as a matter of policy tended to shift support to the social sciences, arts, and humanities as a result of heavy federal financing of the physical sciences and the life sciences.

In considering foundation financing of studies other than the life and physical sciences, the activities of the Ford Foundation deserve special mention. This giant in philanthropy distributed more than $900 million between 1951 and 1957, and of this sum $640 million was given away in 1956 and 1957 (Table 7).[8] Over this period a total of $517 million was provided for educational purposes — $379 million for general education (including a $260 million grant to privately supported colleges and universities to enable them to raise teachers' salaries), $47 million for adult education, and $91 million for medical education.[9] All of these grants have expanded the general capacity of colleges and uni-

69

Table 7. Distribution of Ford Foundation grants by program (millions of dollars)

Program	Grants
Total	143
Behavioral sciences	28
Economic development and administration	27
Humanities and the arts	7
International affairs	26
International legal studies	11
International training and research	31
Mental health	13

Source: Unpublished, undated mimeographed table made available by the Ford Foundation.

versities to finance research in the social sciences, arts, and humanities. More specifically, the Foundation distributed over this period more than $70 million for support of research in the social sciences and smaller sums for the arts and humanities. Virtually all of this money has gone to investigators in universities.

Despite the substantial and rising sums available for research in the social sciences, arts, and humanities, these disciplines are meagerly financed. To demonstrate this, I assume that Harvard University is among our richest universities, and that if research outside the life and physical sciences and engineering is poorly supported there, then inadequacies are widespread among the universities of the nation. At Harvard "formal arrangements for secretarial help are such that only department members with formal administrative responsibilities (department chairmen, laboratory heads, chairmen of standing committees, etc.) are assigned secretarial help in the regular budget. As one man put it succinctly: 'Well, you know, the price for a secretary is an administrative job' . . . When secretarial help is not available, the cost in staff members' time may be quite considerable . . ." [10]

As might be expected, "there is widespread feeling among Harvard faculty members that it is inefficient for the University to pay good salaries to its faculty and then use this high-priced time for work which could be done by lower paid personnel." The University might well retort, however, that it prefers more faculty members of high caliber who waste some time typing than fewer members of lower caliber who are given the resources to produce mediocre work with extreme efficiency.

Money for the attainment of the ideal is not available, and this is the root of the problem at Harvard and at most other universities.

When one considers the important problems facing the world — notably, how to avoid the annihilation of the human race — and when one considers that wars begin in the minds of men, the importance of study in the social sciences, arts, and humanities by people of the highest intelligence is obvious. Why is it that research in these areas is not supported adequately?

The fundamental reasons, particularly in the arts and humanities, relate to the predominant values of our society. Scholarly research in linguistics, in the classics, in fine arts, in literature, are simply not valued highly by the interlocking maze of groups whose attitudes decide how research funds — university funds, foundation funds, or federal funds — are to be distributed, or how university budgets are to be provided among departments. The same attitude towards research in the social sciences has been fairly widespread, as is the notion that social science and socialism have a great deal in common.

These attitudes have become widespread among people in two lines of work which have some common characteristics — academic administration and politics. The following passage, spoken in the course of hearings on the functions of a National Science Foundation, states quite accurately the major premises of many statesmen and scientist-statesmen:

Clarence Brown (Representative from Ohio): "There is a sort of an antipathy against social science, if I can sense the thought of my colleagues properly, that might make a difference in whether this legislation gets not only approval, but prompt approval. I think we had better stick to fundamentals. There are all kinds of social scientists, and there is some question as to just how valuable some of their contributions to the public welfare might be."

Dr. Isaiah Bowman (President, Johns Hopkins University): "Your remarks, Congressman, are in effect a summary of the views of most of the scientists who testified before the Senate subcommittee."

Mr. Brown: "That is a very great compliment."

Dr. Bowman: "We do not think we are so learned. We are just average fellows doing a job."

Mr. Brown: "You are the experts upon whom we must rely."

Dr. Bowman: "It seems to me essentially unsound to put into a National

71

Science Foundation a wide range of social questions upon which the people of America have not yet made up their minds."

Mr. Brown: "That is exactly the point of view which I have, that the average American just does not want some expert running round prying into his life and his personal affairs and deciding for him how he should live . . . there would be a lot of short-haired women and long-haired men messing into everybody's personal affairs and lives, inquiring whether they love their wives or do not love them and so forth . . ." [11]

These attitudes, attenuated and more subtly stated, have had extensive influence on the decisions of universities and foundations. It is well to remember that of all foundation funds for university research, and of all university research funds from internal sources, less than 20 percent is provided for research in the social sciences. Other factors are, of course, involved. For example, university officials often note the aggressiveness of physical and natural scientists as compared with investigators in other fields as fund raisers. Principal investigators and department heads in the physical sciences do, in fact, often appear to be more aggressive, more politically astute, and more willing to undertake the politicking often necessary to obtain funds than have their colleagues in the social sciences. This is somewhat of a paradox. One might expect that the scientists in the physical and biological sciences, lacking formal training in human relations or politics, would be less adept at the maneuvering which often is necessary to obtain funds.

A case can be made for insulating faculty members in the social sciences, arts, and humanities from a time-consuming, distracting, and annoying search for funds. A hunt for research money can become an end in itself, pompous busy work, and a search for bigness for the sake of bigness. But dedication is not synonymous with asceticism. Scholarly productivity is not dependent on poverty, and financial help does not necessarily decrease intellectual freedom.

Factors other than the prevailing attitudes in Congress account for the fact that larger sums are not forthcoming from the federal government for research in the social sciences, arts, and humanities. In the first place, no agency has explicit authority to support research in the arts and humanities. Moreover, the good case that can be presented for the relevance of rigorous work in these areas to the problems facing the federal government is somewhat complicated. For example, the American people and their representatives in Congress have not yet been convinced of the vital significance of having an extensive national research effort dealing with the languages, culture, and history of the Middle East.

In this situation, the federal agencies have moved cautiously into the support of the arts, humanities, and social sciences. For the most part, the projects supported are on subjects of direct interest to the operating missions of the agencies. These include, for example, investigations for the Department of Defense of the characteristics of various kinds of leaders, studies for the Social Security Administration of the prevention and reduction of dependency, and such problems of obvious importance to the public as studies relating to mental health.

The National Science Foundation is permitted but not required to support training and research in the social sciences. The legislative history of the National Science Foundation Act indicates a clear intent to emphasize mathematical, physical, medical, biological, and engineering sciences. This led the Foundation to proceed cautiously in supporting research in the social sciences. After several years of compiling data on support of social science research, the Foundation approved a program of limited support in 1954:

> This limited program is being developed on an exploratory basis within a framework of four criteria. These are:
>
> (1) the criterion of science, that is, the identification, within the social disciplines, of those areas characterized by the application of the methods and logic of science;
>
> (2) the criterion of national interest, namely, the assignment of highest priority to social science activities directly related to the responsibilities of the Federal government with respect to national welfare and national defense;
>
> (3) the criterion of convergence of the natural sciences and the social sciences; and
>
> (4) the criterion of basic research.
>
> The program is being administered within the framework of the Foundation's three scientific divisions.[12]

73

Caution in supporting the social sciences, made particularly evident by stating criteria for support of the social sciences in terms of the direct relation to the responsibilities of the federal government, and burying social science research in fields not subject to attack, has been the general course followed by all federal agencies. The National Science Foundation had to protect its program in the social sciences through such devices at the cost of a tactical modification of the basic research mission of the Foundation.

When the realities of the federal scene are closely observed, and when the roles of universities are examined with care, it would seem not only more feasible but more desirable that an urgently needed expansion of research in the social sciences, arts, and humanities be financed from private rather than from public sources, and that this be done if necessary by re-allocating rather than by expanding university and foundation funds.

Scientists by field

The distribution of scientists among the various disciplines is easily ascertainable.[13] (The distribution of students as contrasted with fully trained persons is discussed in Chapter 7.) Indeed, the shifts in output of manpower by field over time are known much better than are shifts in research expenditures. It is not the shifts but the reasons they have come about which are difficult to determine.

Looking first at broad fields of learning, the proportion of all doctors' degrees granted in the natural sciences had declined since the great depression by about a third — from 44 to 32 percent between 1926 and 1957 (Table A–10). This suggests, but does not demonstrate, that the concentration of federal research funds in these sciences has not resulted in an undue shift of emphasis to these fields.

It would be reasonable, but wrong, to assume that the decline in the proportion of doctors' degrees granted in the natural sciences has been matched by an increase in the proportion of degrees granted in the social sciences, arts, and humanities. The proportion of doctorates granted in these fields has also dropped — from 32 percent to 23 percent between 1926 and 1957.

CHART V

DISTRIBUTION OF Ph. D'S BY FIELD, 1926 - 1957

Post-war decline of natural and social sciences, humanities and arts

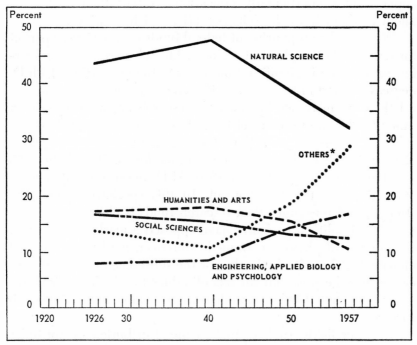

*Health fields, business and commerce, education, law, architecture, journalism, library science and social work
Source: Appendix Table 10

As the proportion of doctors' degrees granted in the natural sciences and in the social sciences, arts, and humanities has declined, what fields have become more popular? The answer is that the proportion of all doctors' degrees that are granted in engineering, psychology, applied biology, health fields, business and commerce, and education has been rising. For example, more doctors' degrees in education are now granted annually than in all of the arts and humanities plus economics and history.

In short, despite the volume of federal funds for research in physical and life sciences, the significant trends in concentration of doctors' degrees by field have not been to the physical and life sciences and away from the social sciences, arts, and humanities.

75

The trend has been from basic to applied fields, and I suspect, from the more difficult to the easier fields. These shifts are in large part the result of an expansion of doctorate training in the applied fields (particularly education), rather than a shift of talent to them from the sciences, arts, and humanities.

Why has the outpouring of federal funds over a 15-year period for research in the physical sciences, life sciences, and engineering not resulted in significant increases in the proportion of Ph.D. degrees granted in these fields? It seems that forces more powerful than the increases in funds for research are at work. As an example, the rapid growth of federal grants for research in medical schools has had no apparent effect on the number of physicians trained (Table A–11). The production of Ph.D.'s in 1955 was four times as great as in 1930; M.D. degrees granted were only 1.5 times the 1930 output. In this specialized area, the strength of forces other than research funds is clear. Strong economic and political pressures have opposed a marked increase in the number of physicians trained. Moreover, neither the general climate of the medical schools, nor the substance of medical education, nor the predominant sets of values to which medical students are exposed have exerted strong pressures toward research careers.

In other fields, such factors as the distribution of aptitudes among groups entering college, the strength of traditions in universities, the cultural background of students, career aspirations, relative monetary rewards by fields, and the general attitudes and values of our society undoubtedly combine to exert stronger pressures than those generated by research funds.

Since these forces are so powerful, the federal research grants and contracts do not appear to be "distorting" the fields of study chosen by graduate students so far as this "distortion" can be measured in numbers of students.

Even though the federal research funds have not significantly affected the broad division of doctors' degrees between the physical and life sciences and other fields, it is possible that the availability of federal research funds may have caused relative shifts among specialties within these fields.

Such shifts come about primarily by influencing graduate stu-

CHART VI

INCREASES IN OUTPUT OF M.D'S AND Ph.D'S, 1930 TO 1955

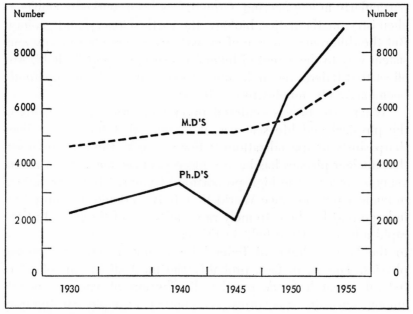

Source: Appendix table 11

dents who are at the stage of selecting a topic for a dissertation, those who are about to decide what and where and with whom to study in the postdoctoral period, and those who are choosing their first jobs. It is at these stages that specialties are explored and tentatively selected. The availability of funds for graduate or postdoctoral study or for research in certain fields can at this stage pull individuals toward certain specialties without "distorting" their interests. Graduate students have always been strongly influenced by faculty advisers. The wise and compassionate adviser will, within fairly wide limits set by the capacity and interests of the student, lead the student toward fields where the prospects for congenial work, for support of research, and for advancement in teaching, seem bright.

The rate of increase in the annual number of doctors' degrees granted has varied markedly among special fields within the

77

broad category of physical and life sciences. For example, the rate of growth has been relatively rapid in astronomy (with very small absolute numbers involved), in physics, in agriculture, and particularly in engineering. Growth has been markedly slower in chemistry, mathematics, biology, the earth sciences, and geology. But the differences in rate of growth are not related in any consistent way to the extent of federal research support by field. Any effect that federal research support may have had has apparently been masked by much stronger forces.

When attention is centered upon specialties within fields of the physical and life sciences, it is clear that there have been sharp shifts in specialization: [14] For example, the obvious guess that nuclear physics has been a more popular specialty in recent years is correct. The high proportion of young physicists trained in nuclear physics since World War II is no doubt accounted for in large part by the extremely rapid advance of the field. But the rapid advance of the field in this case is traceable in large part to the large volume of federal funds for research in nuclear physics. This is, in fact, probably the most significant effect of federal research funds on the distribution of younger people among scientific specialties. As another example, stratigraphy and gas geology are more popular now than in the past. In this case, the federal depletion allowances for petroleum are probably more responsible for the popularity of these fields than are federal research expenditures. As another example, microbiology is an increasingly popular specialty within the biological sciences. Here the development of science combined with extensive federal funds for studies in microbiology probably account for the shift.

All in all, both the growth of science and the availability of federal research funds seem to have affected the career choices of younger scientists. Science is not static. The rate of change in most fields, as measured by the emergence of new approaches, new techniques, and new basic ideas, appears to be as rapid in recent years as in any other epoch. It would be remarkable if these changes were not reflected in the distribution of graduate students among the sciences. In addition, such factors as career propaganda in secondary schools, the influence of a group of strong scientific leaders, and job prospects influence choices of fields of study. Finally, the federal funds have exerted pressures which in part reinforce the movements indicated by the growth of science itself, and which in part set up pressures against these movements.

Shifting from the quantitative to the qualitative point of view, the federal funds have probably not increased the proportion of the most able students who select the physical and life sciences and engineering. One reason for this supposition is that the physical sciences have, as will be shown in Chapter 7, always attracted a high proportion of the most able students. Moreover, specialized aptitudes, academic backgrounds, and attitudes limit the proportion of those entering graduate study who have a free choice of broad fields of study. Dr. Du Bridge has stated the case succinctly:

I can't think of many first-class physicists who would have made very good historians — and I don't know any historians who would have made good scientists. I am inclined to think that the talents required are of rather different kinds and that the chance of very much proselyting one way or the other is not great.[15]

In short, the flow of federal funds into the physical and life sciences has probably not caused a greater proportion of highly gifted students to enter graduate studies in these fields.

Apart from the distribution of younger students by field of science, the federal research funds may have affected the total number of graduate students in the sciences. These effects would be an increase in the general propensity of undergraduates to pick science as a field of graduate study because of the general aura of prestige of science and the plentiful financial support of science as a result of federal activities. But such indirect effects, if they exist, are quite imponderable and impossible to measure.

On the other hand, the federal research funds provide direct financial aid to graduate students in the sciences through research assistantships which provide about $40 million in salaries a year. The effects of these funds on the educational process are discussed in Chapter 7. Here attention is centered on the possible effects of research assistantships on the number of graduate students in science.

Despite the income provided to graduate students through

research assistantships there would probably be no fewer graduate students now if the research assistantships had never existed. (One possible exception to this generalization is the field of engineering. Industrial jobs for students with an undergraduate engineering degree have been more plentiful and better paid than jobs for students with B.S. or M.S. degrees. In the absence of a strong tradition of graduate work, graduate students in engineering must have not only a subsistence but enough financial help to ward off the temptation to leave for an industrial job. The research assistantships have provided this help for many engineers. In fact, the average federal research assistantship for engineering graduate students pays about $2,000 as compared with $1,500 for graduate students in the physical sciences.) The primary reasons for this guess are the healthy state of the economy over the past decade, increasing industrial fellowships, high and rising family incomes, alternative job opportunities — perhaps not as congenial, but a source of money — for graduate students, unused loan funds in universities that would probably be extensively tapped if economic conditions had not been so good, and the likelihood of a further shift of university, industrial, and foundation fellowship funds into physical sciences and engineering if the research assistantships had not been available. Finally, if it appeared that inability of graduate students in the physical sciences and engineering to finance their education were exerting a serious downward pressure on graduate enrollments, more extensive federal aid to students would probably have been made available. These considerations are not conclusive, but cumulatively they are fairly persuasive.

What would be the effect of sudden withdrawal of federal research assistantships? This hypothetical question deserves consideration because there is no certainty that federal funds will continue indefinitely at high levels.

Sudden withdrawal of the funds would, in the absence of compensatory action, play havoc with graduate study in the physical sciences, life sciences, engineering, and psychology. Sudden withdrawal of more than one-fifth of all outside support received by graduate students would leave many without immediate means of support.

This assessment of the probable effect of a reduction in the volume of funds on the number of graduate students is buttressed by the opinions of 131 deans and department heads who were asked to assess the effect of a sharp cut-back (Table 8).

Table 8. Probable effect of reduced federal funds on number of graduate students, assessed by department heads

Department	Percent no effect	Percent sharp reduction	Percent moderate reduction
Total	10	48	42
Physics	0	60	40
Chemistry	0	55	45
Psychology	25	15	60
Mathematics	25	25	50
Bacteriology	0	50	50
Geology	0	25	75
Engineering	10	45	45
Biology	0	50	50

Source: Responses to questionnaire presented in Appendix, Section 2.

These responses, cited more extensively later in Chapter 7, agree with opinions expressed to me in personal interviews. The following excerpts from these interviews are significant because I have not encountered a person close to the university scene who has expressed a contrary view.

The department is able to secure a larger and better graduate student body as a result of Federal contracts. At the moment the chemistry department has about $100,000 a year in contracts. More than half of the graduate students are on stipends derived from Federal contracts. *Chairman, department of chemistry, large state university.*

If research contracts were moved from the department of electrical engineering at ———— State, graduate enrollment would decline by 90 percent. Most of these young fellows are married, and if they can't finance their graduate work they have to leave. *Chairman, department of electrical engineering, large state university.*

There are now one hundred and eight graduate students of electrical engineering at ————, and this number would be cut in half if the federal programs were removed from the university. *Professor of electrical engineering, private university.*

About half the graduate students would have to drop out if federal funds were cut off. *Dean, graduate school, large state university.*

There is an apparent contradiction in maintaining that research assistantships have not increased the number of graduate students but that withdrawal of funds would cause graduate students to drop out. The explanation is that it is assumed that the withdrawal will be sudden. Gradual withdrawal of funds would probably have little effect on the number of students and fields of study, except in engineering.

Since the nation cannot afford a reduction in the volume or quality of graduate education in the sciences and engineering, how could the dangerous consequences of a sharp decline in research assistantships be avoided? In view of competing demands for university funds, the prospect of producing an additional $40 million a year from university funds for fellowships in science and engineering seems visionary. Only about $4 million is available annually for fellowships from institutional funds. Industrial fellowships might be forthcoming in greater volume, but these now total less than $3 million a year after almost a decade of fairly heavy propaganda. Industry would not take over all of the burden.

A substantial expansion of federal fellowship plans would be necessary if graduate enrollments in science and engineering were to be maintained in the face of a sudden cut in federal research funds.

Freedom, direction and excellence

Federal research funds have probably exerted a moderate effect on the distribution of university research by field of science, and on the distribution of scientists by field. In assessing the effects of the funds on the distribution of money and manpower, it is important to bear in mind that the federal money often, although not always, follows rather than leads development in science. It is also important to recall that forces from within universities and from society exert strong pressures towards applied research and towards research in the physical sciences, engineering, biology and medicine. The federal agencies are not autonomous entities but are rather, for the most part, sensitive means of reflecting the dominant values and goals of our society.

5

University Research Costs

Whether universities should participate in covering the cost of research financed by the federal government, and the subordinate question, whether the federal government should pay the indirect as well as the direct costs of research which it finances, have been more extensively debated than any other problem in this field. The intensity with which these questions have been pursued by federal and university administrators reflects the difficult financial position of most universities. They have had no alternative but to press for the collection of the full costs — direct and indirect — of research financed by the federal government. More than a financial question is involved, however. Federal research funds have become so significant an element of the income of many universities that the question of federal control of university research arises. The problem of maintaining the universities' capacity and willingness to sustain a productive balance between research and teaching comes to the fore.

On 10 September 1958, the Federal Bureau of the Budget issued *Generally Applicable Principles for Costing Research and Development under Grants and Contracts with Educational Institutions* (Circular No. A–21), which said that "the extent of agency and institution participation in the financing of a particular research and development project is properly the subject of negotiation between the particular agency and the educational

83

institution concerned." In view of this general policy, it might seem that discussion of cost participation and indirect costs is beating a dead horse. However, the considerations underlying cost participation are worth discussing because they have a direct bearing upon the total relation between universities and the federal government.

As is true with many aspects of federal research in universities, university participation in the cost of the federally financed work can be profitably approached in terms of the objective of the federal agency — purchase of research or support of research. When a federal agency purchases research from universities, federal and university administrators agree that the universities may legitimately demand and that the federal agency has an obligation to pay the full cost of the purchased research. When research is supported rather than purchased, the question of whether the full cost of the supported research should be borne by the federal government is not so easily answered. Basic questions as to the functions and goals of both federal agencies and universities are involved.

Cost participation — equity and freedom

When supported research is indistinguishable from research which the university would be willing to support from its own funds, it can be maintained that any federal supplement is a boon to the faculty members and the university. This supplement permits the university to perform more effectively one of its basic functions, support of research undertaken at the initiative of faculty members and freely pursued by them. The university would normally expect to spend either private income or state appropriations for research of this type. In the face of this normal expectation, it can be maintained that as a matter of equity the burden of university research should not be shifted to the federal taxpayer.

Moreover, when federal agencies offer to support research in universities, the universities are free, so far as the federal agencies are concerned, to accept or reject the support. It can be maintained that if the government imposes a financial burden on a university by paying less than the full cost of research, the university can control the burden by limiting the volume of federal research funds which it will accept.

A third consideration based on equity is related to the incidental benefits received by universities when the federal government supports research. These may include enhancement of the prestige of faculty members and the institution, exploitable patents, support of graduate students through research assistantships, and freeing of general university research funds for departments, notably arts and humanities, which receive little or no federal support. These benefits are real even though they cannot be priced. Universities naturally tend to stress indirect costs but to pay relatively little attention to indirect benefits. On grounds of equity, it can be plausibly argued that universities should pay at least a modest sum for these benefits.

A final consideration based on equity relates to the distribution of research funds among competent investigators and universities. When federal research budgets are insufficient to support all competent research applicants, payment of full costs to some applicants results in denial of any support to some others. Individuals whose applications are denied because no funds are available have no way of knowing that payment of the full cost of research conducted by other investigators is the reason their applications must be denied. More than equity to individuals is involved in this consideration. Payment of full costs might tend to concentrate payments even more highly among relatively few institutions, and the possibility that the research funds might assist to any degree in the development of a more diversified and hence stronger national research structure would thereby be forestalled.

Apart from considerations of equity, compulsory cost participation has been urged as a protection for universities. If the federal government pays the total cost of the research which it supports, the universities might have no incentive to review the research which faculty members propose to conduct with the aid of federal funds. This might, in turn, lead to an imbalance between the research and the educational function and to the conduct of research not appropriate to the university environment.

The final, and perhaps the most significant, consideration in

85

support of cost participation has been that failure of a university to participate in the financing of supported research might lead to federal control of research, exerted through direct dictation of the substance of research. More subtle means of control might include a shift in the investigator's standards expressed in compromises — conscious or unconscious — as to what he will request money for or what work suggested by contracting agencies he will agree to undertake. He may be rushed into publication as a means of increasing the probability that a contract or grant will be renewed, or his time may be controlled by the imposition of a heavy burden of paperwork.

The case against compulsory participation

While the case for cost participation appears quite persuasive, it is open to question. First, the distinction between purchased and supported research, needs reexamination for the problem at hand. Supported research is a concept based essentially upon the work of individual scientists. From this point of view it appears that when the federal government offers to pay the total costs of the research of a faculty member whose work the university would willingly cover if it had the money, the university has abdicated its function and shifted a proper university cost to the federal taxpayer. When one views the total research programs of all universities in relation to the goals of the federal agencies, however, the situation appears quite different.

The sum total of all federal programs for support of research in universities can be considered a declaration of national objectives and an expression of national policy. This policy is made particularly clear by the willingness of Congress to appropriate funds for the support of university research which has no immediate relevance to the operating tasks of the federal agencies and to provide funds to expand the nation's research resources. Participation in this national effort involves many universities in uncongenial large-scale research, and it creates new academic and financial difficulties for them. The total effect of the federal activities is not entirely to help the universities do more of what they wish to do, but to involve them in the achievement of national goals which they did not set. This involvement can come about for a university as a whole even though the effect of the federal funds on individual faculty members is to help them do precisely what they want to do.

It is not valid to argue that the national interest, expressed as the operating needs of a federal agency, is served when research is purchased, but that the national interest, expressed as further-ance of free research with no necessary relevance to the operating needs of federal agencies, is not served when research is sup-ported. Equally significant national needs are met through the two different types of financing. Faculty members whose free re-search is supported serve the interest of the nation as surely and perhaps more importantly than when they undertake contract re-search at the urging of a federal agency.

The fact that research of the type traditionally supported as a prime function of universities serves the national interest does not establish a case for payment by the federal government of the full costs of the research it supports in part. On the other hand, the fact that general national interests are served by the prosecu-tion of such research does indicate that payment of full costs by the federal government should not be precluded on the ground that such research is a normal function of universities.

Universities which conduct research financed by the federal government not only serve the national interest in various ways, but typically undergo changes in doing so. Heavy involvement in research financed by the federal government has changed the essential character of many universities. The expanded research has made the maintenance of a sound balance between teaching and research difficult in some cases, and impossible in others. The imposition of a qualitative change on universities as a conse-quence of undertaking federally financed research strengthens the case for payment of full costs by the federal government.

The federal funds for support of research must be viewed not only as a prize to a faculty member but as a powerful and perva-sive influence upon the university as a whole. Only when atten-tion is centered on the prize aspect of federal research support does cost participation by universities appear imperative on grounds of equity.

Nevertheless, if universities are free to reject the federal research funds, a major premise of the argument for cost participation, any adverse effects of accepting the money would appear to be the responsibility of the universities. While no university is required by law to undertake research for the federal government, whether universities are in fact free to refuse federal research grants and contracts is a complicated question.

As was pointed out in Chapter 2, many universities are and should be responsive to public needs and desires. State universities, for example, have a strong tradition of service to the more immediate needs of the federal and state governments. When such universities undertake large research programs, they are not abandoning academic ideals but accepting a responsibility. In addition, many private universities have felt that they could not deny to the federal government the services of scientists with capacities uniquely fitted to cope with problems on whose solution not only the national well-being but national existence might depend.

On the other hand, some universities, particularly the relatively rich private universities, hold firmly to the view that they serve the long-run interests of the nation, as contrasted with the short-run operating needs of federal agencies, most effectively by accepting only the volume of support that will strengthen the university intellectually, and only the kind completely congenial to the faculty. The reasoning is consistent with and part of the case for a strong system of private universities independent of the federal government.

But if all universities adopted the policies designed to strengthen a few private universities — and in so doing made themselves able to serve the national interest in a unique and indispensable way — the final result would be to reduce the nation's capacity to conduct research.

Other universities accept large volumes of federal funds rather uncritically not because of a carefully reasoned and carefully administered concept of public service, but because they either have no policy or have a policy of growth. But even with such reservations, the universities of the nation cannot be viewed as agents free to participate in or to refrain from research financed by the federal government.

Apart from the obligation of universities to accept federal research funds, they face compelling practical realities. Once a few large universities have accepted federal research funds, the pressures on most others to accept funds are almost irresistible. The federal money buys equipment, space, and supplies which attract good faculty members. Most large universities would have a difficult time recruiting and keeping a full faculty of high quality without federal research funds as long as other universities accept the funds.

Most universities are not in fact free to reject all federal research funds. They must perform the research and take the consequences.

There is little doubt that many intangible benefits are received by universities when they accept federal funds. These benefits are real, but the intangible contribution which universities make to the effectiveness of federally financed research must also be considered. The federal government is in effect purchasing a part of the total services of a going intellectual concern when it makes a grant or contract for research. Federal agencies turn to universities as sites for research because universities are intellectual centers. It costs money to establish an environment which contributes to productive research. On this ground, the federal government should contribute to the maintenance of the university as a whole. Since neither the intangible benefits received by universities nor their intangible contributions to research can be measured, one may assume as a practical matter that they cancel each other out.

The final consideration of equity rests on the fact that full-cost payments, by financing some research completely, reduce the number of research projects that can be financed at least in part. This effect gives rise to inequities only if those whose research is not financed at all have some right which has been violated, or if some violence is done to a proper objective of the federal system. Under the existing system of federal support of research in universities, the amount received by any university is the sum of the amounts provided to faculty members by the judgments of their peers. Research funds are not provided to the university itself. When payment of full costs reduces the number of research grants and contracts that can be awarded, the projects which have not

89

been financed are those of lower merit. Provided the judgments as to merit are sound, those persons who do not receive funds have not been treated inequitably. As long as the basis for distribution of funds is the merit of the individual and the research proposal, those universities which receive less federal research money as a result of payment of full costs are not treated inequitably. A tendency of full-cost payments to concentrate, or to fail to disperse, federal research funds among institutions would be inequitable only if wide dispersal of funds were an objective of the system. This is not now the case, as was pointed out in the discussion of concentration of federal research funds in Chapter 3.

Cost participation, it will be recalled, has been urged not only on grounds of equity, but also on the ground that participation by the university in federally financed research protects the university. While the protection argument is plausible, it is based on premises that are false.

Take first the assertion that cost participation is a means of ensuring that universities will examine more closely the effects of federally financed research upon the content of the institution's research program, upon the balance between research and teaching, and upon the interrelations between research and teaching.

The fault in this line of argument is that universities have the most urgent reasons, unrelated to sources of funds or to the cost-participation policies of outside sources of funds, to assess the total effects of research upon their structure and function. A decade of experience with a policy of full-cost payment by the Department of Defense indicates that the general tendency of universities is to strengthen the review process and to increase concern over the total effects of the federal funds on universities. The insistent problems of institutional policy assert themselves, and are dealt with, under all financial arrangements between universities and the federal government.

There remains the question, which is a key one, as to whether payment of the full cost of research by the federal government will not lead to federal control of university research.

To begin with, it would be difficult to establish that there is a high positive correlation between the degree of danger of loss of freedom and the proportion of support provided from nonuniversity sources. Take some examples cited earlier in another context. Of all university research in physics, 96 percent is financed by federal agencies. Of all university research in the life sciences, 50 percent is financed by federal agencies. Of all university research in the social sciences, 25 percent is financed by federal agencies and 50 percent is financed by private foundations and other private gifts; only 25 percent of university research in the social sciences is financed from university funds.

It would be difficult to present a persuasive argument to the effect that postwar research in physics in this country is more controlled by the federal government, or less productive, or of a lower intellectual caliber, or more threatened with federal restrictions, than is research in the life sciences or the social sciences. The problem is not answered by reiterating that "he who pays the piper calls the tune."

When cost participation is urged as a means of protecting the freedom of the university, it is often assumed that universities should contribute to the cost of research undertaken under each federal research grant or contract to ensure that the university, and the faculty member directly concerned, will thereby be in a stronger position to resist any effort on the part of federal agencies to control that research. Such a scheme is not realistic, however.

If a federal agency were to attempt to interfere unduly with the research of a faculty member, the fact that the university paid 10 or 20 percent of the cost of the research would not substantially affect the situation. Indeed, compulsory cost participation is as likely to restrict as it is to protect the freedom of universities and of individual faculty members. For in many cases, university resources devoted to participation will be secured by reducing the volume of research supported entirely by the university.

If cost participation in each project will not protect the university from federal control of supported research, what will protect it? A university which wishes to retain a substantial degree of freedom for its total research program should attempt to finance a substantial part of all programs entirely from nonfederal resources. These include endowments, current individual or corporate gifts, state appropriations, and other nonfederal sources.

The decisive factor is the proportion of the total research enterprise of the whole university financed by the government, and not whether the federal government finances wholly or partly that portion of the institution's research to which it contributes. For example, in many universities the degree to which faculty time and attention, equipment, and space is committed to federally financed programs is a serious problem. A very heavy commitment to federal research decreases the control that a university exercises over its own affairs by reducing the ease with which the total volume of research and lines of investigation can shift in response to the needs of the investigator and the institution.

The ability to change — an important aspect of freedom — depends more heavily on maintenance of diversity in sources of support for research than on paying from university funds a small part of the cost of each federal research grant or contract. It is doubtful whether the attitude or the power of either the university or the federal agency is significantly altered by changes in the proportion of the cost of specific projects that are government financed. Freedom depends more heavily on the terms and conditions under which federal grants and contracts are offered: it depends more on the stability of support, the latitude given to faculty members to follow new leads, and the extent to which the time of faculty members is consumed in negotiating with federal agencies and in writing reports than on the proportion of each research grant or contract financed from university funds.

Universities have so little money of their own to invest in research that they must rely on factors other than provision of funds to retain adequate control over their research programs. Chief among the means universities can use to maintain their independence when well over half of their research funds come from external sources is insistence upon provision of money under satisfactory terms and conditions.

The effectiveness with which a university bargains for suitable terms and conditions is, in fact, the major protection of its independence. The institutions hold high cards because they are where brains are found. The federal agencies must seek out intelligence and bargain on the terms and conditions acceptable to good investigators. A university with a strong faculty and a social climate which values intellectual excellence highly is more likely to retain the essentials of independence, even when the research is wholly financed by federal funds, than is a university with low intellectual standards, even if it contributes substantially to federally financed research.

There seems little doubt then that universities can, by adoption and enforcement of sound policies, retain a high degree of control of their own affairs in the face of extensive federal financing of university research.

Voluntary participation

The argument advanced above leads me to believe that all federal agencies should offer to pay the total cost of all research which they purchase or support in universities. By 1959, this had in fact become the policy of all major federal agencies except the Public Health Service.

Some universities wish to participate in the financing of research supported by federal agencies because they feel that cost participation is equitable or prudent. Moreover, there are special circumstances, such as provision of funds under circumstances conferring solid benefits upon a university, under which federal agencies should urge universities to participate in the financing of the federally financed projects. But this participation should be voluntary and negotiated.

Indirect costs — definitions

Many universities which are willing to pay part of the cost of research financed by the federal government have objected strenuously to the policies of federal agencies which not only force them to participate in financing research, but require that the participation take the form of university payment of the so-called "indirect" costs of research. University participation has, in fact, often been discussed in the past almost entirely as if the question at issue is only whether the federal government should pay the indirect as well as the direct costs of research.

In order to determine the total cost of research in universities as well as to understand the rather involved debates over who

93

should pay the indirect costs of research, the meaning of "direct" and "indirect" research costs must first be clarified.

Direct research costs are incurred by a university solely and demonstrably as a result of undertaking additional research. Although such a definition is not entirely unambiguous, direct costs of research can in practice be isolated quite precisely. They include the salaries of persons employed specifically to conduct the research for which funds are received, the cost of materials, supplies, and equipment, and a variety of less significant expenses, such as shipping charges, and sales and social security taxes.

Indirect costs of research are those attributable partly to research and partly to other activities. Indeed, a more descriptive name for indirect costs is "joint" costs because the key notion that distinguishes direct from indirect costs is that the direct costs are incurred solely as a result of research while the indirect costs are kinds of costs arising from two or more activities.

Costs may be classified as indirect or joint on a number of bases. A given service may be rendered to the university as a whole rather than restricted to research activities. The university purchasing office, mail and delivery service, engineering office, and similar services are drawn upon to help the research function as well as the educational function. Laboratories have to be maintained and serviced, but typically laboratories are occupied by people whose work is not, as well as by people whose work is financed wholly by the federal government. University laboratories housing federal research are often maintained and serviced by staffs which serve whole departments or even the entire university. Laboratories housing federally supported research are usually heated by plants built to serve the university as a whole.

A given service may be provided specifically to one part of the organization, but the service may be of benefit to all. For example, a university counsel may be instrumental in winning rights to a patentable invention made by a group in the physics department, thereby establishing a generally useful precedent.

If the research activities of a university performed all of these services for themselves, rather than rely upon central services, the costs would be direct rather than indirect. But this would be grossly uneconomical and in the case of some services — such as the operation of the president's office — impossible. Thus, organizational forms that serve in one context to promote efficiency and the effective attainment of institutional goals create in another context a difficult cost-accounting problem.

A distinction must also be made between "incremental" and "nonincremental" indirect or joint costs. Incremental joint costs of research are those involving additional university expenditures. Such costs are incurred, for example, when the research financed by the federal agencies requires expansion of the university telephone exchange, or extension of parking facilities available to all faculty members, or when additional cleaning people have to be hired. Nonincremental joint costs are those that do not require additional outlays by the university. For example, although the president of a university typically spends some of his time attempting to establish university policy toward federally financed research and to resolve operating problems, an additional president is not engaged because of the research problems.

Indirect costs are generally spoken of as if they were all incremental, but the question arises as to whether nonincremental costs should not also be considered as indirect costs. Take the cost of operating the president's office as an example. Since federally financed research does not require a university to engage a second president, the time spent by a president in dealing with problems created by federal research funds costs the university nothing additional. It might be argued that no share of the president's salary should be considered an indirect cost of research. On the other hand, one might also argue that the federal government should pay for the time spent by the president in dealing with problems created by federally sponsored research because he might have spent the same time on other university affairs. The question is whether only additional outlay by the university, or a fair price for any time and effort and resources devoted to the federal research programs, should be the basis for computing indirect costs.

The answer depends upon which of two pricing concepts, defined most precisely in decades of public utility rate-making, is accepted. The first of these is that the consumer should have to pay only what it costs to produce the specific units which he uses. This line of reasoning gives rise to such practices as low long-distance toll rates at night and sale of electricity at low rates to industrial users in off-peak periods. In both of these cases, a system involving heavy fixed costs is operating below capacity and additional services can in this circumstance be provided at small additional cost. The special rates are not based entirely upon the cost of producing the last or "marginal" unit of service but a concession is made to the existence of exceptionally low marginal costs.

The second pricing concept is that a product has a value to a consumer which he should pay even though it costs the producer very little to turn out the specific unit sold. The price which the consumer should pay in this situation is generally defined as approximating the average cost of producing all units.

Public utility regulatory bodies seek essentially for an answer to whether the price to a group of consumers should be based on the fair value of the product or service provided, or on the cost of producing it. The ultimate outcome is a compromise between equity to the producer and equity to the consumer. There is, therefore, no unique, definable best compromise.

The university is analogous to the producer and the federal agency is analogous to the consumer. A university can be considered an economic entity, an enterprise with heavy fixed charges over the short run. When it operates below capacity, it can perform additional service at low cost, or in some cases at no cost.

A decision to pay only incremental indirect costs would be based upon the assumption that the proper function of indirect-cost payments is to avoid forcing educational institutions to spend their funds for the conduct of research performed under grant or contract for the federal government. If this assumption is made, it follows that nonincremental joint costs should not be paid to universities because such costs do not require the university to incur cash outlays specifically as a result of conducting the federally supported research. In terms of cost terminology, this theory is applied by collecting marginal rather than average indirect costs.

A decision to pay nonincremental as well as incremental indirect costs is based upon the assumption that the proper function

of indirect-cost payments is to cover a fair share of the total indirect contributions of the university to the conduct of research
whether or not this contribution necessitates a cash outlay by the
university. This is in effect a theory of pricing based on value
received, and is applied by collecting average rather than marginal
indirect costs.

Should nonincremental indirect-costs be paid to a university, it
would receive indirect cost payments even though acceptance of
the research funds had not required the university to spend an
additional penny. The university would be saying in effect, "The
federal government is using parts of this institution and should pay
a fair price for the use. This value provided to the federal government exists whether or not it costs us additional money to provide
it."

As in the case of public utility rate determination, there is no
unique, definable best answer to this question. The problem of
nonincremental indirect costs has, in fact, not always been recognized and this has given rise to much talking at cross purposes
between university representatives and those of federal agencies.
The university representatives sometimes justify payment of indirect costs by arguments relating solely to incremental costs, and
in practice press for payment of nonincremental costs which they
feel by instinct to be equitable.

At this stage of the argument, it should be clear that there is
no distinction in concept between the reality of direct costs and
indirect, or joint, costs. It has been argued that indirect costs are
not actual costs, but a kind of cost-accounting legerdemain. Those
who take this view have naturally argued that the federal agencies
should not pay the indirect costs of research which they finance.
Most prominent among this group are faculty members who view
payment of indirect costs by the federal government as an unfair
diversion of funds intended for research to the general operation
of the university.

Here it must be admitted that the determination of indirect
costs is both complicated and arbitrary. For example, how much
of the cost of a university library should be attributed to the conduct of research is difficult, if not impossible, to establish precisely. This is true, in varying degrees, of most joint costs. Even

if a precise division of costs could be made, the expense of determining the division would often be prohibitive. For this reason, simplified means of arriving at a division of indirect costs between teaching and research have been developed. These formulas, originally based on arbitrary factors, were extensively revised as the result of an extensive joint study by universities and federal agencies over the period 1956–1958.

The imprecision inherent in indirect-cost determination has led some observers to the conclusion that all indirect costs are not real costs but a tricky means of inducing the federal government to contribute to the general expenses of operating universities. It is well to bear in mind, however, the distinction between the concept of indirect costs and the results produced by any specific formula for dividing these costs between research and other functions. If it is admitted that joint costs are as real as direct costs, then the problem is not one of principle but of the mechanics of determining how the costs are to be divided.

Effects of indirect-cost payments on universities

The indirect-cost policies of federal agencies are important to universities for three reasons. First, and probably most important, universities need the payments. Second, university relations with federal agencies are affected by indirect-cost policies. Finally, indirect-cost payments affect the internal operation of universities.

From a purely financial standpoint, indirect-cost payments on federal research grants and contracts are a significant item in university finances. Indirect-cost payments approach $50 million a year, about $30 million for research centers and $20 million for research connected with university departments. Universities could not absorb $20 million in costs a year without running into severe difficulties.

In the special case of the medical schools, the 15-percent, indirect-cost policy of the National Institutes of Health, in effect through June 1959, provided them with about $10 million a year (assuming NIH research grants at a level of about $130 million a year, of which 50 percent goes to medical schools). Adoption of a full indirect-cost policy at a rate averaging 25 percent would add about $6.5 million a year to the free funds of medical schools. In view of the fact that the primary source of private funds for medical schools, the National Fund for Medical Education, gave the schools only $2 million in 1957, the concern of medical educators over the level of indirect-cost payment is understandable. From the point of view of the schools, all that the private gifts through the National Fund have done is to provide $3 million of the $5 million which the schools now provide from general funds to cover indirect costs of federally financed research.

Apart from the financial question, indirect costs of research create problems within universities. Three of these are particularly important. Should the receipts be held centrally or should they be distributed in whole or in part to the points within the university where the research responsible for the indirect costs is done? If some of the receipts are held centrally, should they be merged with other university funds or should they be placed in a separate account? For what purpose should the indirect cost receipts be spent?

Some administrators are reluctant to discuss how they handle the money. This reluctance is understandable because the financial affairs of all large universities are difficult to understand. Moreover, in some universities sharp differences of opinion between the central administration and the faculty about the proper use of payments inhibit discussion. The relations between state universities and state legislatures create another reason for reticence. Indirect-cost receipts from the federal government add to the general operating funds of the university. Even though payments are intended to cover only the increase in operating expenditures occasioned by acceptance of federal research contracts, many state universities are apprehensive lest the state legislature decrease the university appropriation by an amount equal to the federal indirect-cost payments. For this reason, few, if any, state universities segregate the volume of indirect-cost receipts in their published financial statements or in the budget documents prepared for the legislature. There is, in fact, no reason in accounting or normal budgetary practice for indirect-cost receipts to be segregated when other details of the research grant and contract receipts from the federal government are not. But the fact that indirect-cost receipts are available for general university expenditures nevertheless creates apprehension.

Despite some reticence on the part of university administrators in discussing indirect cost receipts, a few generalizations appear warranted. It should be noted that indirect-cost payments are made as the result of an official determination by a federal agency that a university has incurred costs for which it should be reimbursed. In this situation, the manner in which the university accounts for and uses the funds is not the formal concern of the federal government. Informally, however, federal auditors observe how indirect-cost receipts are spent when they are segregated. One university, for example, built a radio station from indirect-cost funds. Another university has reserved part of a series of large indirect-cost payments from the Atomic Energy Commission to finance the construction of a new wing. There is no regulation, no reason in law or ethics, why indirect-cost receipts should not be expended for such purposes. But one practical result of such concrete demonstrations of the magnitude of indirect-cost receipts has often been the re-examination of the indirect-cost formula by the contracting agency.

Since where a man sits generally determines where he stands, the use of indirect-cost payments is often the source of a running debate between the central administration, deans, department heads, and individual investigators. On the one hand, many faculty members think indirect costs are a "subsidy" or "profit" to the university. Every dollar of federal funds, they believe, should go specifically and directly for the support of research. Many scientists see the payment of indirect costs to the university as legalized robbery, with the business officer, financial vice-president, or whoever it may be, as the thief and they themselves as the victims. On the other hand, the central administration of a university sees the institution in its entirety, and knows where the relative needs are greatest — whether extra funds should be used to reduce the backlog in the library bindery, whether to rewire a building whose circuits are overloaded as a result of research expansion, or whether to pave a parking lot to accommodate the extra employees hired to work on research contracts. Hence, central administrative offices wish to retain control of the indirect-cost receipts so that the most urgent needs of the entire university can be met first. The deans of colleges see critical needs in their departments and press for allocation of part of the funds to use as they see fit. Department heads see their faculties as the individuals whose capabilities bring research grants and contracts to the university. At the same time, they see needs within the department that could be met if the university would hand over to them all of the indirect-cost receipts relating to contracts and grants awarded to members of the department.

Many university presidents, caught in this cross fire, find that the distribution of indirect-cost receipts among competing claimants within the university poses more of a problem to them than the failure to collect full costs.

Ways of reconciling these conflicting interests differ. At one extreme are universities in which deans, department heads, and individual faculty members support general university use of indirect-cost payments. This rare situation seems to depend on the existence of four factors: (a) a university of fairly small size, (b) a strong sense of university loyalty as contrasted with department or laboratory allegiance, (c) an intelligent, persistent, and effective effort to explain frankly to the faculty the financial position and needs of the university, and (d) relatively adequate research funds from university resources. When one of these elements is missing, strains are likely to arise. If all are missing, the stresses between individual faculty members on the one hand and the administration on the other are likely to be severe.

Although many deans, department heads, and faculty members have managed to obtain a direct allocation of some indirect-cost payments, in most universities the payments are held centrally. Research centers and medical schools are, however, exceptions to this generalization. Even when closely associated with a university, the research center usually retains indirect-cost payments on its contracts. In most instances, the federal government pays the entire cost of operating the center. The medical school typically controls payments made on research contracts and grants made to its faculty members. Since virtually all medical schools receive large subventions from a parent university, this is largely a bookkeeping matter because a reduction of the income of the medical schools through central control of indirect-cost payments would probably result in an increase in the general university support of the medical school.

Most universities simply merge indirect-cost receipts with general income from other sources. The indirect-cost payments become part of a common pool, and the ultimate use of the indirect-cost receipts cannot be determined.

Even though most indirect-cost receipts are pooled for formal accounting, many universities informally allocate some or all indirect-cost receipts to the general university funds for the support of faculty research mentioned in Chaper 4. A quite common effect of allocating the receipts in this manner is to free university research funds for stronger support of research in the arts and humanities than would otherwise be possible. This allocation of indirect cost receipts is made not only to aid research but also to ease the strain between the central administration and the faculty.

Other universities have set up separate organizations or even nonprofit corporations distinct from the university to administer federal research contracts. These separate organizations, discussed in Chapter 10, serve as agents of the university in executing and handling all of the paperwork connected with contract administration. They also receive the indirect cost payments on all contracts. Part of the payment is used to cover the cost of operating the separate research organization. The difference between indirect-cost receipts and the cost of operating the separate organization is returned to the university, which then retains part of the money to cover general expenses of the university and returns the remainder to the departments which have research contracts. In some universities, this division of funds is made by the separate organization itself with the help of an advisory board of the university. This "holding company" device is a means both of centralizing and handling efficiently a complicated administrative task, and of keeping indirect-cost payments distinct from state appropriations.

6 ←——————————————————————

Terms and Conditions

The terms and conditions under which federal research funds are provided are significant not on administrative grounds, but because they are the most important way in which the federal funds affect the freedom of investigators. (As with virtually all aspects of government financing of research in universities, the terms and conditions under which funds are made available to research centers associated with universities differ fundamentally from the terms and conditions under which funds are made available to other parts of the university or to individual faculty members. The research centers generally operate under master contracts which set a broad mission for the center as a whole. The degree of freedom of the individual investigator in a research center is more a reflection of the philosophy, scientific capacity, and administrative skill of the leaders of the center than it is of the terms of the master contract with a federal agency.) Is the investigator free to wander where leads may take him, or must he follow a predetermined line and seek the answer to a predetermined problem? To the extent that federal funds restrict the ability of scientists to go where their minds lead them, the funds limit freedom. Is the investigator time-bound — forced to plan and execute his work within a fixed time span? Is he kept in a state of uncertainty with respect to the continuation of federal research? To the extent that he is, the federal funds in a sense control scientists. Is the scientist able to communicate more or less effectively with his colleagues as a result of federal financing of research? Ability

103

to communicate is an absolute prerequisite to freedom of research. Finally, is the scientist required to conform socially or politically as a condition of receiving federal research funds? To the extent that he is, the federal funds interject an element of control over individuals that is antithetical to freedom of the mind and to effective research.

All of these influences on the freedom of the individual are exerted quite apart from the substance of the research on which he is engaged. Even if an investigator is engaged in "basic" research, he can hardly be called free if he has to spell out in detail what he wishes to do, justify fully any alteration of his plans, write detailed quarterly reports of progress, supply lengthy justifications for his expenditures, plan on the assumption that support may be curtailed at any time, and prove his political conformity.

The project system

Research which is supported or purchased by a federal agency is described in a contract or grant and often referred to as a project. For example, the Public Health Service must by law support research through research "projects," and while the National Science Foundation is not required by law to support research projects, it has elected to do so.[1]

The project system has been roundly condemned. Many trenchant criticisms have laid bare the substantive matters which must be wisely dealt with if federal support of university research is to be productive. These criticisms have been succinctly stated in a well-known essay by ex-President Dodds of Princeton:

The phrase 'project research' has come to describe a special pattern of research undertakings in which the source which furnishes the funds does so with the understanding that the research will be directed to solving a problem in a specific area which has been mutually agreed upon in advance.

With the abundance of project research money currently available, we are in danger of succumbing to a new disease for which no antibiotic drug has been discovered; namely, 'projectitis.' Projectitis is an unhappy addiction to limited objectives, perhaps at the very moment at which the individual should be broadening his own comprehension and deepening his knowledge of his discipline, with freedom for roving speculation in an atmosphere unencumbered by the pressures of problem-solving commitments to external agencies.

Competent observers are particularly concerned regarding the effect of over-indulgence in projects upon our young scholars and scientists. They fear that there are a goodly number of such throughout our universities whose future contributions to learning are being reduced by preoccupation with the limited objectives of project research . . .[2]

The project system has also been severely criticized in the somewhat more specialized context of medical education. A study made for the American Medical Association reported:

Such methods of support inevitably lead to direction of research by agencies outside the medical schools and result in regimentation of the faculty and loss of freedom to follow their bent and their own clues to new knowledge. The compulsion and lack of freedom increase when he is compelled to report the results of his research to the grantor at regular intervals . . . There is a tendency to isolate the project or develop a research institute . . . Although such projects may strengthen certain small areas in a medical school, they certainly add little to its over-all strength or balance.[3]

The AMA study did not define a project, but by implication the authors identified a project as anything except free funds for general support of the medical school, for they noted that the need of the school "is for institutional — not project — support."

From the foregoing observations it is clear that the term "research project" has been used with many meanings. The confusion that can result from the word "project" is illustrated by the manner in which the Committee on Institutional Research Policy of the American Council on Education introduced its discussion of project support:

In general there are three methods under which sponsored research is carried on in colleges and universities. These are: grants to individual faculty members on the basis of proposals initiated by them; grants to institutions which are either uncommitted as to fields or projects or made for work in specified broad fields; and grants to individuals or institutions in support of specific projects.[4]

This exposition implies that a project cannot be initiated by an investigator and that project support for work in broad fields does not exist. These are conditions contrary to fact.

The fact that "project" has many meanings suggests that the

important question is not whether federal agencies supply funds to universities under a project system but the substantive characteristics of the forms of support. Discussions of federal support of research in universities would be much clearer if attention were centered not on the word "project," but on the important, measurable characteristics of federal support which determine the degree of freedom of the recipient of federal funds. The most important of these are breadth and stability of support.

Before turning to these characteristics of the federal systems, however, one major question of policy deserves discussion — whether the man or the project should be supported.

"Support the man, not the project"

Perhaps the academic scientist's most persistent criticism of the project form of support has been that it tends to concentrate attention upon what a man has done, what he alleges he is going to do, and the elegance with which he sets forth his allegations. The view is widespread that: "The choice before us, experimental design or free research, the project or the man, has many ramifications, but it concerns the mainspring of the entire operation, the future of research in America. Let us support the man." [5]

The major premise underlying this view is that the federal government is seeking to advance science, rather than to purchase a specific finding. When research is purchased, however, the government's interest is in the findings not in the future of research in America. The man is important in this circumstance only in relation to his capacity to reach the specified objectives effectively, quickly, and economically.

Relations between the granting agency and the applicant for funds, and between scientific advisers to the agency and their colleagues who apply for funds, dictate that the nature of the proposed research veil any judgment on the capacity of the man. Anyone who has many ideas need not be offended by a judgment that one of his ideas is not worthy of support. He can always be consoled by the belief that more ideas will be forthcoming, that the advisory group did not understand the significance of his proposal, and so on. But an investigator who knows he has been denied support because of a general judgment as to his competence has

106

been dealt with brutally. Moreover, a judgment based solely on competence is more difficult and delicate than an assessment of the worth of an idea, particularly when younger investigators are concerned.

While the two types of judgments may in fact be similar, there is an elaborate apparatus of "objective" factors — research design among them — for obscuring the subjective element in decisions on the substance of proposals. To the extent that judgments are based on the estimated capacity of individuals, maintenance of the fiction that the basis of judgment is the research proposal is almost essential to the operation of the system. Persons whose applications are denied can then view with adequate equanimity not only the fact that they were denied funds but also the fact that other people received them.

Not all scientists are good enough to be supported as individuals apart from what they propose to do. When the scientific men must be sorted from the scientific boys, it is almost imperative to have a device which will permit those who lose to accept the decision. Reliance on the substance of proposals is that device.

The second political factor dictating support of the project rather than the man arises from the fact that Congress, the public, scientists, and some federal administrators, tend to consider federal support for scientists as a personal subvention. Of course, the only reason for aiding scientists is that as a group they will produce some kind of benefit to the community. The benefit need not necessarily be in terms of a bigger bomb or a new vaccine. It may be an intellectual ferment or the valued pursuit of one aspect of truth, and the best way to go about producing the maximum benefit for the community may be to support the competent individual and to let him then decide what he will do. But if this is done, there exists no tangible evidence of benefit to the community. In this circumstance, support appears to be a personal subsidy which the scientist uses not only to pursue the work he selects but also work of no necessary relevance to the needs or desires of the community. The form of support for the work provides the needed symbol, even when the actual and proper basis for decision is primarily the known capacity of the individual rather than what he proposes to do.

107

It is for reasons such as these that federal agencies, even the National Science Foundation, must stress in public pronouncements the relevance and quality of the proposed research rather than the ability of the investigator.

A real problem is to give adequate weight in substance to the ability of individuals when preponderant weight must be given in form to the nature of the proposed research. Advisory groups generally work out this problem, although the relative ease of relying upon the nature of research exerts a constant pressure toward inadequate emphasis upon the ability of individuals as the basis for judgments.

It would be a harsh though justified critic who said that this complicated play of forces requires federal agencies and their scientific advisers to be hypocritical. It is more realistic and productive to observe that the difference between form and substance, between words and action, is a social and political device serving an essential function. Stress on the substance of research rather than on individuals is perhaps the only way of showing laymen who provide the money how the research expenditure serves a social purpose; and stress on the significance of research proposals to those who apply for money is perhaps the only means of operating the system without generating explosive pressures from within the world of science.

Within this somewhat ritualistic performance, the capacity of individuals and groups is in fact given much greater weight than one would assume from the written policy statements of the federal agencies.

Breadth of support

The general trend has been towards the adoption of contract and grant terms providing for progressively broader definitions of research, partly in response to representations from universities, and partly because the federal agencies have gradually seen that their objectives are more effectively attained by broad definitions of research. The terms and conditions have evolved gradually with little or no change in written policies. Thus, the Public Health Service now supports for sustained periods some broadly defined areas of investigation. These are called project grants although they have few if any of the undesirable characteristics often attributed to project grants. Other agencies which use the contract device have similarly broadened the kind of work covered by contracts without segregating funds, inventing a special name, or otherwise calling attention to their course of action. The principal device is the so-called master contract which sets a broad research task for a university group. Subtasks are then negotiated informally or formally through amendment of the contract. The cumulative result of this process has been a general broadening of the scope of contracts and grants, provision of funds in larger amounts for more generally defined work, and assured support over longer periods. The degree to which this has taken place is often underestimated.

Discussion of the breadth of research financed by individual federal research grants or contracts is somewhat complicated by a semantic problem, particularly when research is supported. Alternatives to project support are called variously, block grants, free funds, fluid funds, program grants, departmental grants, and institutional grants. The import of all of these terms is that funds are provided by the federal government with few strings attached. Often they have no specific meaning but are used loosely and interchangeably to denote terms and conditions more to the liking of the recipient.

A group studying support of the social sciences pointed out this semantic problem and proposed a solution:

> It may well be that the very use of such terms as 'fluid grants,' 'general support,' and 'free funds' is in itself a major obstacle to a solution of the problems we are posing . . . What is really needed for the development of research is not 'free funds' . . . It is support for fields or clusters of research interest in which the University has developed plans, but not for highly specific projects to which it cannot and should not commit itself in advance.[6]

In general, evolution of the federal grants and contracts has in fact been towards "program" grants in the physical as well as the social sciences. The focus of attention remains the individual or group, but the task for which funds are made available is defined more broadly and greater latitude to shift emphasis within the broad area is permitted.

While the question of the breadth of the research to be supported by federal grants and contracts is generally discussed in terms of the needs of the individual scientist for freedom and stability, wider issues are involved. Various groups of people in universities want funds to be distributed so that they can control the money. Individual investigators, for example, generally prefer research funds to be made available directly to them. But a system of grants and contracts built around the individual investigator, no matter what the size of the grant or contract may be, has a tendency to make the relation of the federal government to universities in fact the relation of a large number of subordinate federal officials to a large number of faculty members. In the process, the faculty members are likely to instill a point of view in the officials. Relations between federal officials with broader responsibilities for the total effects of federal funds on universities are in general not nearly so close as those between faculty members and officials engaged in the day-to-day administration of grant and contract programs. A system built around individual scientists tends by its nature to forestall an effective working relation between federal officials with responsibility for general decisions and their counterparts in universities.

Department heads quite often express a desire to be permitted to distribute federal funds in accordance with the needs and capacities of all members of the department. The department head's plea for freedom often looks to the individual faculty member like a maneuver to deprive him of freedom. Deans and university presidents in turn view federal research funds in the light of the problem which are most significant to them. They ask to be allowed to distribute at least a part of the funds to solve more general university problems. The federal agencies are inevitably drawn into, and help to decide, this contest for power which exists in many universities because the broader the definition of research, the higher is the point in the academic hierarchy at which research funds are controlled.

As a rule, the higher a person stands in the academic hierarchy, the more acute is his sense of the problem of sustaining balance among the major functions of the university, the less does he view research as a self-contained function, and the more is he concerned with research in the context of the total role of the university. In contrast, the federal agencies look primarily to the performance of a research mission when they provide funds for research, and any consideration which they can give to the functions of the university as a whole must be within the context of the research objectives.

As research is described more generally, its relevance to the mission of the federal agency becomes progressively more difficult to demonstrate, and its relation to the educational as well as the research function becomes clearer. Indeed, broadly defined institutional research grants could have the character of general support to universities. This possibility was pointed out in a discussion of block grants for medical research at a recent international conference:

> In general, the Conference disliked the suggestion that the central organization might give block grants to universities if the grants were, in effect, general subsidies. Such a suggestion could only arise when the income of the university was insufficient for the discharge of its duties. A university has many functions, of which the free pursuit of research on an adequate scale is one. Research organizations, on the other hand, are concerned with one particular purpose, the promotion of research. At any one time, their policy is determined by their assessment of the changing priorities in the research field itself. This may not necessarily coincide with academic needs so that the central organization — however sympathetic to the university's case — may feel compelled to refuse applications for general support or to grant them only under conditions which limit the university's freedom of action. Further, from the point of view of the research organization itself, it was inappropriate to undertake continuing commitments of this general nature. The essential role of such an organization in relation to the universities is to be complementary; to this end it is essential that it should maintain its finances in a flexible state so as to remain free to take advantage of opportunities and to meet new needs as they arise. The Conference concluded, therefore, that it was undesirable that universities should look to research organizations for support by block grants.[7]

There is always the possibility that the existing system of research support, which is operated essentially by the combined efforts of federal officials and university scientists and administrators, may be replaced by a system under which research funds — particularly for supported research — would be distributed by formula. This prospect is viewed with aversion by both university and federal representatives, not only because it would remove most of their influence over the system but also because it would shift attention from the merits of individuals and ideas. The prime feature of the existing system which serves as a barrier to the distribution of federal research funds by formula, and to pressures from congressmen to help institutions in their states, is emphasis upon the project and upon the individual scientist. The more the current system moves toward block grants to universities with increasing emphasis upon the educational as well as the research function, the greater the pressure and, indeed, the logic of shifting the criterion of distribution to a formula measuring the total financial needs of universities.

The most important policy question arising from federal support of research in universities is whether the specialized aid should be broadened to, or supplemented by, general financial aid to higher education. This question has arisen most directly and acutely in the field of medical research. The schools, public and private, are inadequately financed. At any given time, one or more schools is on the verge of closing because of lack of money. But the total capacity of the schools must expand, or more schools must be established, merely to sustain the current ratio of physicians in the population. While the educational budget is starved, the research and research training budgets are opulent. As a result, an appreciable part of the private and public funds provided for research actually supports the educational function with the tacit acquiescence of those who provide the research funds. This situation is awkward in some respects, but not illogical. Direct federal support of medical education is not a step to be taken lightly. The federal research and research training funds are a useful means not only of supporting these vital functions of medical schools but also of providing a means for testing the effects of general federal support of higher education in a circumscribed area.

Stability of support

The most important factor influencing the stability of research in universities is the fate of the budgets for the federal agencies. Prudent administrative practices can mitigate the disruptive effects on university research of moderate reductions in these budgets, but sharp reduction in the funds for any agency would interrupt research, create difficult personnel problems, and cause financial troubles for some universities. Fluctuations in the research budget of parts of the Department of Defense have been particularly troublesome. So far as medical schools are concerned, half of their separately budgeted research is financed by research grants and administered by the federal National Institutes of Health. Marked instability in the form of large and unexpected increases in the budgets of the National Institutes of Health by Congress over the decade 1950–1959 have generated problems for medical schools, primarily because the agency has not paid the full costs of the research which it has supported. On the other hand, a sharp drop in the budget of this agency would not only completely demoralize medical research but would seriously jeopardize the financial status of the medical schools as a whole.

In connection with stability of research support, the one-year budget cycle of the federal government is often singled out as the major source of difficulty. The more fundamental source of such budgeting instability as has existed has, however, been the absence of stable policy in the executive branch. Congress has been notably willing to support research on a sensible basis, and has in fact — a few aberrations excepted — acted more consistently than the executive branch.

Even if the budgets of federal agencies are stable, the support of individual investigators will be unstable if the agencies decide to provide only short-term support — for example, a year with no renewal. Under these conditions, investigators must tailor their work to fit within a year or two, and this tends to channel and restrict work. Moreover, a grant for a one-year period hardly enables work to begin before the worry over renewal starts, and this distracts the person in charge. Finally, the scientist is led to view his career as a discrete series of short-term, self-contained tasks rather than as a sustained exploration of an area of science.

When support is for a substantial period, another aspect of stability emerges — how long before expiration the decision on renewal is known. Even if a research grant or contract is ultimately renewed, investigators pass through a period of uncertainty if they do not know, well before the expiration date, that funds will be forthcoming. Furthermore, if the faculty member is unable to make a firm commitment to graduate students because of delay in making money available, either they cannot be brought into the research project work, or the investigator must make and break commitments to successive groups of students. It is not unknown for a faculty member to be forced to raise and dash the hopes of three or four groups of graduate students while awaiting a final decision on a contract renewal.

For all of these reasons, decision on renewal should be made, and made known to investigators, at least a year before the expiration of a grant or contract.

When research support is not stable for any reason, the director of a large laboratory must often spend a good share of his time in seeking new sources of money, in shifting money from one pocket to another, in transferring people from one payroll to another, and in general in acting like a citizen caught by a loan shark. The anxious atmosphere is not conducive to productive work.

While no one has a claim upon a permanent livelihood at the taxpayers' expense simply because he is engaged in research, concern for the productivity of the tax dollar warrants assurance of a reasonable period of support.

The one-year budget cycle of the federal government influences the stability of federal research support. Agencies can and do, however, routinely make and fully honor advance commitments to support large numbers of investigators for years. The research agencies are not in fact faced each year with the possibility that Congress will abolish research funds, even though cuts may be made. By giving a carefully regulated volume of long-term commitments a first mortgage on future appropriations, administrators can assure stable support even though annual appropriations fluctuate.

When research is purchased, the length of time required to complete the task at hand determines the duration of support. A federal agency which purchases research has no responsibility for the difficulties faced by the investigator or the university when the stipulated research task is completed. The direct obligation is to get the most and best research for the smallest expenditure of the taxpayers' money. In this circumstance, the needs of investigators and universities collide head-on with the responsibilities of federal agencies.

When research is supported rather than purchased, the situation is different. Research is supported not to provide data or devices needed by federal agencies, but to advance knowledge in various fields of study. Consideration of the conditions best calculated to foster scientific work leads to the conclusion that sustained research, rather than research arbitrarily broken into projects of limited duration and scope, is required for effective performance.

The fact that sustained aid for individuals is desirable in order to support fields of research suggests that the best way for the federal government to aid research would be to provide funds for permanent research posts. This is not practicable now, and it may never be. The reasons for its impracticability illustrate some limitations inherent in federal support of research. Some scientists begin as highly productive investigators, only to fizzle out. So long as support of research is the federal mission, an accounting at reasonable intervals is a reasonable requirement. And if a group of competent and reasonable men find that the investigator is not productive, it is reasonable to stop the support. It may well be necessary to underwrite more university research careers which continue to provide status and income whether or not the investigator continues to produce as a scientist. But when the federal government's function is the support of research rather than the support of all functions of universities, support should not extend beyond the period over which the scientist is productive. As a practical matter, assured duration of support for five years with one-year advance notification on renewal would appear to provide a reasonable standard of stability.

Perhaps the most important limitation on the duration of support is set by the volume of funds available to the federal agencies. Assurance of support for several years in advance reduces in any one year the volume of money available to those to whom advance commitments have not been made. If an agency has been operating on a stable budget for research grants of $10 million a year and the average duration of grants is two years, $5 million a year is available for new grants. But if the average duration of grants is five years, only $2 million a year becomes available for new grants. With an increasing budget it is possible both to extend the average period of support and to make a substantial number of new grants or contracts. With a declining budget, however, heavy continuing commitments may wholly eliminate new grants or contracts. The funds available for new grants are the funds from which promising younger investigators and new ideas are financed.

To ensure that some funds for new grants will be available even if the budget is cut, the prudent administrator generally restricts the advance commitment of funds. In this process, the administrator must listen both to those who tell him of the critical importance of stability of support and to those who tell him of the key significance of watching for the promising younger men. In his capacity as intermediary, he must be able to explain why neither goal is completely attainable except in the unusual circumstances when funds are available to do both.

In short, no single objective can be pursued to the exclusion of other equally significant objectives. The problem of the research administrator and his advisers here, as in other areas, is usually not the achievement of a single objective but the attainment of a tentative, shifting, workable compromise between equally sound and sometimes mutually exclusive goals.

Federal research and scientific communication

Federal agencies often require reports on the progress of research which they finance. The frequency, detail, and purpose of these reports depend for the most part upon whether the research is purchased or supported. When a federal agency purchases research, it may expect the end product to be either some tangible object or a report of findings. The agency may well wish and may legitimately require progress reports on how work is proceeding. A number of projects may be interrelated, and the rate of progress on one task may affect others. Progress reports are a means of integrating such research. In addition, progress reports are a means of checking on whether the purchaser seems to be getting his money's worth.

The essential problem is to make the reporting system a useful tool for assessing the progress of work, for reporting findings, and for communicating scientific information. Sometimes such requirements as quarterly reports on research progress appear to university scientists to be designed more as a means of protecting federal administrators than of communicating meaningful and usable data, and sometimes they are right.

On the other hand, some research reporting systems are a means of transmitting findings in a fast-moving field much sooner than would be possible if publication in the professional journals were relied on. For example a valuable reporting system in the field of nuclear physics has been financed by the Atomic Energy Commission to supplement the private journals. Such federally financed *ad hoc* channels for reporting scientific findings are a means of supplementing the archaic methods and the inadequate resources of the standard scientific journals.

In the long run, new patterns for classifying, storing, and retrieving scientific information will have to be devised. These will involve drastic changes in the nature and function of professional scientific journals. Federal financing, in whole or in part, of a new system of scientific communication appears to be inevitable. Unless the journals change drastically, large federal subsidies to permit prompt and full publication appear to be the only means of solving a problem which has grown steadily worse since the beginning of World War II. And in this connection, the means devised to prevent federal control of investigators while the federal government is financing the research should be adequate to forestall federal control of publication after the work has been completed.

Secrecy and security

Among the most controversial terms and conditions for federal research funds supplied to universities has been the requirement that some research be kept secret and that faculty members engaged in unclassified research meet some obscure standards of "security."

University scientists have been uniquely qualified to conduct some research which must be kept secret because potential enemies might benefit if the findings were revealed. Most universi-

117

ties which have accepted contracts for classified research have done so for the same reason that they have accepted contracts for any federal research — a sense of obligation. Moreover, universities have understood and accepted the fact that the trustworthiness of faculty members with access to classified research should be proved by an investigation of their past actions, their reputation, and their associations. Secrecy, however, is inimical to the freedom of communication which is prerequisite to scientific progress. Hence, secret research is essentially alien to the university environment.

Fortunately, only about 15 percent of the $140 million in the federal research funds supplied for university work outside the research centers, including the funds spent under Department of Defense and Atomic Energy Commission contracts, is for classified research. The special research organizations, and particularly the research centers, have served as the sites of most of the secret work carried on for the government by scientists associated with universities. These organizations have been the primary means of lessening an apparently serious threat to free communication among university scientists during the years immediately following the war. In lessening the problem, however, the deadening influence of secrecy on research has not been exorcised, only transferred.

The requirement that faculty members conducting unclassified research with the aid of federal research grants and contracts meet standards of "security" or "loyalty" set by federal agencies is in concept quite distinct from the conditions imposed to preserve military secrets, and has posed deeper and more complicated problems.

Federal research funds for unclassified research have been denied to university scientists who have been charged with political unorthodoxy, improper associations, past contributions to currently unpopular causes, and leftist tendencies. Denial of these funds has posed the only serious threat of federal control over universities and university faculty members, and has created the only fundamental difference between the federal agencies and the universities in the postwar period.

The threat arose initially because some federal agencies acted purportedly to protect the security of the nation by refusing to pay federal funds for unclassified research to persons adjudged to be disloyal, or to be a security risk. As an incidental by-product these goals may have been achieved, but they were not in fact the determinants of the action. The policy which determined the specific acts was to avoid trouble with some senators. Frequently the actions taken with respect to individual scientists in universities were not guided by the terms of any written and generally known policy. The criterion was less often a threat to the security of the nation than a threat to the personal security of administrators at all levels or to the security of the programs of the executive branch against retaliatory action by Congress. In this atmosphere, calm and wise decisions made under procedures sustaining a reasonable balance between the rights of the individual and the needs of the state were not to be expected.

Perhaps the most prominent example of zeal to avoid criticism from Congress by ensuring that all recipients of federal research funds were politically impeccable was the policy of the Department of Health, Education and Welfare. On 28 April 1954, the Secretary of that department issued a press release which defined for the first time in writing the principle employed by the department in deciding whether grants, virtually all of which were for unclassified medical research, should be withheld on the ground that the applicant or recipient was disloyal or subversive. The press release read in part as follows:

> We do not require security or loyalty investigations in connection with the award of research grants. When, however, information of a substantial nature reflecting on the loyalty of an individual is brought to our attention, it becomes our duty to give it most serious consideration. In those instances where it is established to the satisfaction of this Department that the individual has engaged in or is engaging in subversive activities or that there is serious question of his loyalty to the United States, it is the practice of the Department to deny support.

The application of this policy depended first upon the fortuitous availability of information and second upon the judgment of departmental officials as to what acts would cause "security officers" to question seriously a person's loyalty to the United States. Those who made initial judgments and final decisions were not inclined to endanger the nation, their budgets, or themselves by establishing lax standards of loyalty for medical research scientists. Denial by the Public Health Service of medical research grant funds for unclassified work to some individuals who continued to receive research contract funds from the Department of Defense, and particularly the shadowy procedures and elusive criteria associated with denial of grants, created a furor in scientific circles.

The National Science Foundation courageously took the lead among the federal agencies in stating formally a set of reasonable criteria. On page 8 of its Annual Report for the year ending 30 June 1955, the Foundation said that it would not give grants to anyone established as being a Communist or anyone convicted of sabotage, espionage, sedition, or subversive activity. The Foundation also said that if substantial information indicated that a potential or actual researcher might be guilty of violating any law or regulation, it would not cut off grant support but would forward information to the Department of Justice for appropriate action.

Despite the soundness of this general approach, not until 1956 was reasonable normalcy approximated. Indirectly, the only formal censure of one of its members by the Senate in recent years, a stronger stand by the administration, and a combination of public apathy and public revulsion were responsible for the change. More directly, intervention by the White House changed and clarified the policies and actions of the agencies in the direction first set by the National Science Foundation.

On 11 January 1955, the Assistant to the President requested in a letter to Dr. Detlev W. Bronk, President of the National Academy of Sciences, "that the Academy counsel with the government on its policy with regard to relations between questions of loyalty and the awarding of government grants and contracts in support of unclassified research." The academy appointed a distinguished Committee on Loyalty in Relation to Government Support of Unclassified Research under the chairmanship of J. A. Stratton, Chancellor of the Massachusetts Institute of Technology. On 13 March 1956, the Committee submitted a forthright document that cut through a maze of obscure, inconsistent, shifting, and half-articulated and half-secret policies and practices of the federal agencies. The summary findings and recommendations of the group, which were a major factor in the return to sanity, were as follows:

1. The test in the award of grants and contracts for unclassified research should be the scientific integrity and competence of the individuals responsible for carrying out the research, and the scientific merits of their program.

2. When an official of the Government comes into possession of evidence which in his opinion indicates the possible existence of disloyalty in violation of law, he should promptly refer that information to the Federal agencies of law enforcement established to deal with such matters.

3. An allegation of disloyalty should not by itself be grounds for adverse administrative action on a grant or contract for *unclassified* research by scientifically competent investigators; if the indications of disloyalty appear sufficiently serious to warrant any action at all, the Government in the opinion of the Committee has no other course than to bring formal charges and to produce the evidence in open hearing before legally constituted authority.[8]

These findings, in part a ratification of a changed situation but in larger part an act of leadership, led to a new pattern among the federal agencies which followed in principle the criteria suggested by the committee.

The security clearances for unclassified research in universities have led me to speculate over the state of affairs that would have existed if the federal government had been financing the universities themselves, rather than the research conducted there.

As a general matter, there are weighty reasons for believing that federal financing of higher education need not be followed by federal control. Fifteen years of financing of research with no federal control suggests that general aid could be provided without deadening uniformity, control of curricula, or federal selection of faculty. Even more impressive evidence that federal financing of higher education need not be followed by federal control is provided by decades of experience under the system of grants for colleges of agriculture and the mechanic arts.

The one occurrence that has shaken my conviction that general federal aid to higher education poses no inherent danger to the freedom of universities has been the imposition of security

121

clearances for those engaged in federally financed unclassified research. This whole episode in our history, now happily past, is repugnant because it involved an essentially immoral abandonment of the values without which our form of government and indeed our society cannot survive. The dignity of man was submerged, for rationality and freedom were abandoned. The hard search for a workable balance between the rights of the individual and the needs of the state was temporarily abandoned. No margin was allowed for human fallibility and frailty. There was at the height of the fever little personal moral responsibility, tolerance, compassion, or wisdom. If general federal aid to higher education had been in force over the period 1951–1956, the freedom of American universities would have been seriously threatened.

The significance of the great security-loyalty aberration was not, however, that federal aid to higher education inevitably means federal control through one route or another, but that no sector of our society can remain untouched by the great surges of fear, suspicion, hate, and anger that accompany war and the slow return of peace. Many universities, it should be remembered, were not overly vigilant in defending the values to which they are ostensibly dedicated when defense of wrongly accused faculty members endangered private gifts and state appropriations. Indeed, the backlash of the security-loyalty programs entangled even the great private foundations.

With this clear example of political control in mind, should the possibility of federal control arising from some such development as the security clearance procedures be grounds for rejecting federal aid either for research or for general operating funds? I do not think so, for I believe that this nation possesses the political and administrative devices, and the common sense, to provide federal funds to universities without imposing harmful controls.

7

Graduate Study

While federal research funds flow to universities to finance research and not education, it would be remarkable if the large volume of research funds did not affect the educational process. Fear that these effects have been adverse has been fairly widespread. In 1949, for example, the Chief Scientist of the Office of Naval Research, Alan Waterman, later the first director of the National Science Foundation, expressed an apprehension that has been felt by many observers:

> Increased support of research in universities has been accompanied by an increased number of graduate students. What effect will this have upon the quality of the doctor's or graduate engineer's degree? It may be that by increasing graduate school enrollment we shall succeed in turning out no larger number of potential research leaders, but shall actually lower the average competence of the total output, by dilution and by congestion.[1]

This chapter is devoted essentially to an examination of the question posed by Dr. Waterman, and as background some facts are presented before the main questions are dealt with:

What is the general sequence of graduate studies?

How many graduate students are there; how intelligent are they?

What and where are they studying?

Sequence of graduate studies

In the first and often in the second year of graduate study, the work of students is concentrated heavily upon mastery, on a more advanced level, of fields covered in undergraduate years. Typi-

123

cally, the graduate student works more independently than the undergraduate although the degree of independence varies among fields and among universities. Attendance at organized, scheduled lectures and in classes becomes less important as the student assumes a greater degree of responsibility for the direction and pace of his own work. The object is to give students the theoretical background indispensable for independent work at later stages.

During the second year the student begins to cast around for a subject for his dissertation. He may select a subject and begin the experimental or other work required. In the third year, formal courses will have become less important, or will have ceased entirely, and virtually full time will be spent on the dissertation. Usually, the dissertation will be completed during the third or fourth year of graduate work.

At all stages of his work, a graduate student should as an ideal be free to concentrate entirely upon his work without having to make a living. The faculty has the problem of guiding students who must earn money currently if they are to pursue graduate work, and of deciding at what point the distractions of earning a living are so great that the student cannot be considered as moving at an adequate pace toward his academic goal.

Quite commonly graduate students are attracted by the reputation of the university as a whole or of a particular department. Often the attraction is to a certain man or a group. After beginning graduate study, it is common for a student to move into the intellectual orbit of a faculty member and to be guided in the choice of a specialized area of work either by his general influence or his specific suggestions.

From this brief note, some of the points at which federal research grants and contracts may impinge on graduate study can be seen. The research grants and contracts can absorb the time of faculty members, reducing the time which they have available for instruction of graduate students. Conversely, the work on federally financed research can make teaching more lively. The presence of federally financed research can create opportunities for work on material suitable for dissertations. These work opportunities may be a contribution or an impediment to a fully effective graduate career.

The number of graduate students

In 1954, undergraduate enrollment in the United States was approximately 2 million. In that year, there were between 200,000 and 225,000 graduate students, or roughly 10 percent of the number of undergraduates (Table A–12). Since the proportion of undergraduates who go on to graduate study changes slowly, it may be assumed that in every year since 1954, the number of graduate students has been about 10 percent of the number of undergraduates. In 1958, when there were about 3.5 million undergraduates, there were probably about 350,000 graduate students.

About a quarter of all graduate students are in the physical and life sciences and in engineering.[2] About 40 percent are in education, and somewhat fewer than 15 percent are in the social sciences. The remaining 20 percent are in various fields.

About 60 percent of all graduate students are in the first year, but the proportion of graduate students who are first year students varies widely by field: in education, 75 percent; in engineering, 60 percent; and in the life and physical sciences, 40 percent.

Given the needs of the country, there are not many graduate students. Many of those who are enrolled are not engaged in rigorous advanced study, many study only part time. And numbers are not the most important thing. The importance of the tasks that require advance study makes the capabilities of students and the quality of the instruction of graduate students critically important.

The intelligence of graduate students

Whether federal research money has attracted an increasing proportion of bright students to the physical sciences and engineering is an important question. But before this question can be answered, it is necessary to know something about the intelligence of students at various levels.

If federal funds for research do attract the more intelligent groups of students, the process probably begins at least at the undergraduate level. Undergraduates specializing in engineering, mathematics, and the physical sciences are by far the most intelligent undergraduate groups, as measured by the Army General

125

Classification Test (AGCT), the test used during World War II on all recruits.[3, 4] More than two-thirds of them scored 130 or better (Table 9). (The AGCT has been calibrated so that the

Table 9. Percentage of undergraduates scoring 130 or higher on the Army General Classification Test [a] by field of study, 1951

Field of study	Percent of students scoring 130 or higher
All fields	50
Biological sciences	46
Engineering	67
Physical sciences and mathematics	68
Humanities	48
Social sciences	51
Education	20
Business and commerce	43
Agriculture	29
Miscellaneous	29

Source: Educational Testing Service, *A summary of statistics on Selective Service college qualification tests of May and June 1951*, Statistical Report SR-52-1 (Princeton, N.J.: Educational Testing Service, 1952), p. 69 (Tables 6 and 12).
[a] Actually Selective Service College Qualification Test converted to equivalent AGCT scores.

mean score of the entire population is 100. Sixty-eight percent of the population has scores between 80 and 120. Only 5 percent of the population scores 130 and higher. Only 25 percent of all college graduates will score 130 and higher, and this is the average score of all Ph.D.'s. Only 1 percent of the population will score 147 and higher, and only 0.1 percent 160 or higher. The average score of all graduate students is 124, a score that is achieved by somewhat less than 17 percent of the population.) Undergraduates in the social sciences were the next highest. Only 20 percent of the students in education scored 130 or higher.

The differences in score between the engineers and physical scientists and the other undergraduate groups as shown by the tests is so striking that they probably reflect real differences. Perhaps the great demand for qualified engineers and scientists, created in large part by federal research grants and contracts draws a large proportion of intelligent undergraduates into these fields. Or it may be that higher intellectual ability of the kind measured by the tests is required in these fields. Probably both factors are operating.

The high proportion of intelligent undergraduates among the

engineering and natural science majors raises the question of whether these groups are attracting too many of the most able young people. What "too many" might be is hardly measurable, but a meaningful and answerable question can be posed: Do all of the major areas of undergraduate study attract a substantial number of young persons of high intelligence? The answer is yes. In no broad area of undergraduate study did fewer than 20 percent of the seniors score below 130 on the AGCT.

Thus, even if it were true that the demand for natural scientists and engineers biased the choice of undergraduates, there is no doubt that every field of undergraduate study attracts highly competent people. "Each field gets some members of only mediocre quality. But each also gets some who are able to exercise the kinds of intellectual leadership which are indicated by high scores on tests of intellectual ability." [3]

On the graduate level, differences in intelligence are less marked than among undergraduates. In the only comprehensive study of this subject, the median score of graduate students in all natural sciences combined was 128. The median scores of other groups range from 121 in education to 132 in psychology (Table 10).

Table 10. Median test scores of persons with Ph.D. degrees and of graduate students, by field of study, 1947

Field of study	Graduate students	Ph.D.'s
All fields	124	130
Natural Sciences	128	133
Engineering	126	133
Psychology	132	137
Social Sciences	124	——[a]
Education	121	——[a]

Source: Table A-13.
[a] Not available.

The top 10 percent of the Ph.D.'s in the physical sciences and engineering are a group of very bright men and women. All of them are in the top 1 percent of the population in intelligence. From this group our scientific leaders will emerge. On this group universities will depend for outstanding teachers. This is the group from which industry will draw the most creative scientific and technological talent. This is the highly select group whose training is of the utmost importance to the future of research in this country. At any one time in recent years only about 6,000 graduate students in science and engineering comprised the group, distributed by field roughly as follows: 1500 in the life sciences (biology, 1100; agriculture, 400); 2500 in the physical sciences (mathematics, 400; physics, 640; chemistry, 1,030; other, 430); and 2,000 in engineering.

Later in this chapter, the effect of federal research funds on the training of this group of exceptionally able graduate students, a matter of extreme importance, is specifically examined.

Concentration of graduate students

A few universities have always awarded a high proportion of the Ph.D. degrees in this country. In the academic year 1955–56, for example, only 158 colleges and universities awarded a Ph.D. degree. Within this group, 9 universities awarding 200 or more Ph.D. degrees granted 36 percent of all Ph.D. degrees (Table A–14).

Ph.D. degrees in special fields of science and engineering are concentrated to a remarkable degree in a few universities. For example, of 511 Ph.D. degrees in physics awarded in 1957–58, 51 percent (236) were awarded by 15 universities.[4] Together, California, Columbia, Illinois, Michigan and Harvard Universities, and the Massachusetts Institute of Technology awarded 124 Ph.D. degrees in physics in 1957–58, or 27 percent of all such degrees conferred by all universities. The same pattern appears in the life sciences. For example, one-third of all degrees in biochemistry (52 out of 149) were granted by the universities of Wisconsin, California, Minnesota, and Purdue. The study of mathematics is also highly concentrated. Half of the 210 Ph.D. degrees granted in mathematics in 1957–58 were granted by 11 universities.

The most significant direct repercussions of federally financed research on the educational process are felt in relatively few universities.

Research assistantships

The federal government is providing funds for a graduate "earn-while-you-learn" program which is substantially larger than the total of all direct fellowships financed by the federal government, for 20,000 to 30,000 graduate students earn about $40 million a year at these jobs.[5]

The research assistantships are an outgrowth of the research grants and contracts. When a university submits a contract proposal or an application for a research grant to the government, it outlines the expenditures required for the proposed research. Among the items of expense almost invariably listed is one for technicians and other people who will help the scientists responsible for the investigation. Some of the supporting staff are graduate students with scientific backgrounds ranging from elementary to quite advanced. They are called research assistants. They perform tasks varying from routine manual labor to full scientific collaboration with senior faculty members.

Once a contract is let or a grant is made, the selection of individuals to fill the positions itemized on budgets is left to the scientist responsible for the research.

Research assistants do not receive stipends, but are employees working for wages or a salary. Accordingly, the research assistantships are in form quite distinct from fellowships. In substance, as will be shown, the differences are often not clear. For this reason, the research assistantships must be integrated with all other forms of financial aid available to graduate students if the total student-aid of a university is to operate smoothly.

The university (or the department or the professor, depending upon the practice of the university) is free to decide not only whether graduate students will be employed but what they will be paid. The university also fixes the relation that will exist between the job and the graduate student's education. The federal government is interested only in whether the university, as a spender of tax money, gets value received for the wages paid.

About half of the research assistants are employed in the physical sciences — divided evenly between physics and chemistry. Twenty-five percent work in the life sciences, and 20 percent in engineering. Only 5 percent are employed in the social sciences and in fields other than science.

While fewer than 10 percent of all full-time graduate students hold federal research assistantships, these include about a quarter

129

of those in the physical sciences and a third of those in engineering. Universities tend to reserve research assistantships for advanced students. Thus, in the physical sciences 14 percent of the first year but 29 percent of the advanced students held research assistantships.

The median annual income per assistant from federal research assistantships, typically earned over a nine-month period, exceeds $1,600.[2] Earnings in the nonsciences, however, are only about $1,000 per year, while the median research assistant in engineering earns more than $2,000 per year.

The substantial income earned by individual graduate students as research assistants has created two significant problems.

First, as research assistants some students earn as much as or more than they do later as instructors after receiving the Ph.D. degree. A professor of physics stated the problem to me this way: "The ability to earn a fairly decent salary for graduate students so early in their graduate careers gives some of the boys a false sense of financial security, and they get married only to find that they cannot sustain the income that they secured in the second and third graduate years." I suspect, however, that such psychic wounds as arise from premature affluence heal quickly.

Second, and more important, the federal funds available for research assistantships have made it difficult for many universities to achieve a balance between research assistantships and teaching assistantships.

Ideally, week-to-week, face-to-face teaching in the classroom should be by mature and experienced faculty members. (Some universities hire teaching assistants not for classroom teaching, but for grading of papers, preparation of laboratories for laboratory sessions, and similar chores not involving face-to-face instruction of undergraduates. Teaching assistants of this type neither affect the quality of undergraduate instruction nor gain real experience in teaching.) This is a luxury which many universities cannot afford, and the graduate teaching assistant is a device widely adopted (see Chapter 8) as the next best thing. The assistants hold classes in which lectures given by senior faculty members are discussed, and in which texts and other written material relating to the course are reviewed. They also guide students in

130

laboratory work associated with undergraduate courses. Those who guide undergraduate students in these classes should be chosen from among the best graduate students.

Since the salaries of research assistants come from plentiful federal research funds and those of teaching assistants from scarce university funds, one would expect that research assistants would be paid more. The median teaching assistantship pays in fact about $1,200 a year, while the median research assistantship pays about $1,600. Since the research assistantships not only pay more but are otherwise more attractive, the best students tend to take these jobs. The problems created thereby for universities are obvious, and comments like the following excerpts from personal interviews are typical:

> The graduate student prefers a research assistantship to a teaching assistantship both because it pays more money, and because it moves him forward more rapidly toward his degree. Fellowships are practically nonexistent in electrical engineering. — *Dean, school of electrical engineering, large state university.*
>
> The average ability of the teaching assistant has declined. The shortage of teaching assistants is particularly acute in physics, chemistry, and engineering. The shortage is attributable to the availability of research employment. — *Dean of the graduate school, large state university.*

The potential or actual discrepancies between the pay of research and teaching assistants as well as the relation of both kinds of jobs to the educational process force most universities to consider how the two earning-learning experiences are to be used in helping graduate students. Many universities consider the academic capacity and economic needs of each graduate in the development of plans of study, stipends, work experience, and earnings. One university, for example, has an institution-wide contract committee which considers not only the substance of contracts which the institution should accept but also the placing of graduate students on teaching and research assistantships. The timing, volume, and nature of work as a research or teaching assistant are tailored to the development of the individual student. No faculty member may hire a research assistant without the approval of the committee. There is no financial pressure on the student to prefer one kind of assistantship to another because the pay is the same for equal amounts of work. Firm limits are set on the amount of time a student may spend as a research or teaching assistant.

Under a second pattern, research assistantships are considered solely as sources of income for graduate students, without relation to the students' academic development and with no control over the relative earnings of research and teaching assistants. (At one university which follows this pattern, graduate students are permitted to work 40 hours a week in a federally financed laboratory associated with the university. This work need have no relation to the students' academic work. The laboratory and each university department have their own rules on the limitations to be set on earnings and working time of research and teaching assistants. Throughout the university the pay for teaching assistantships is lower than for research assistantships.) When this pattern is followed, difficulties arise out of the lowered quality of teaching assistants and out of poor guidance of graduate students. These are matters to be resolved by universities and not the federal government.

Dissertation by contract

Much research financed with Federal funds involves a number of significant lines of investigation that are fit subjects for doctors' dissertations, and many graduate students who work as research assistants turn the work that they are paid to do into their doctoral dissertations.

University policies toward the preparation of dissertations based on work as a research assistant range from flat prohibition to complete acceptance. Flat universitywide prohibitions against the preparation of dissertations with the aid of research grants or contracts are rare, but an occasional department does prohibit the practice. (Most universities will not accept a thesis containing secret information derived from work on a federal research contract, a so-called "sealed thesis," because a doctoral dissertation is supposed to be a contribution to knowledge judged by a group of faculty members and available to the world. Since a sealed thesis can rarely be read as a whole by a group of faculty members, and circulation must be limited, the entire spirit and purpose of doctoral study is thereby distorted. There are few such dissertations.) The Department of Biology of the California Institute of Technology issued a policy statement on 30 April 1952, which provided that, "No work done by a graduate student employed by his major professor for which the latter acts as Responsible Investigator will be accepted by the Division of biology as material for the doctoral thesis." Generally, however, graduate students are permitted to use work done on federal research grants and contracts as a contribution to dissertations. Quite commonly, the student is permitted to use data he has collected while working under a contract as the basis of his dissertation, but he is required to analyze and write up the data on his own time. At some universities a student may explore ideas arising out of grant or contract work as the groundwork for a thesis, but he will not be paid from contract or grant funds for collection or analysis of data. He may, however, freely use the equipment and facilities made available in whole or in part through federal research funds. In other universities the student may be paid while he collects, analyzes, and writes up data, and he may use clerks and stenographers who are paid from federal funds. The proportions of universities or departments which follow these various policies are not known.

Earning and learning

University policies vary widely with respect to the time that graduate students may spend on outside work. At one extreme are strict, fixed limitations on the amount of nonacademic work a research assistant can accept, established because the administration believes that nonacademic work should not prolong graduate study unduly.

The California Institute of Technology has such a policy. All employment not connected with the Institute is frowned on. Research assistants may work a maximum of fifteen hours a week during the school year on research contract work, but the Department of Biology does not permit graduate students to work for pay at all on any grants or contracts held by members of the Department. Fifteen hours a week is considered the maximum which an average student can undertake without jeopardy to his mental and physical health or to his academic standing and progress. In the summer, graduate students may work up to 30 hours a week for 15 weeks. Employment of graduate students in this circumstance is simply a chance to earn additional money in a job more congenial than that of waiter or laborer. Such a policy would, if universally adopted, prevent many competent students from pursuing graduate study unless other sources of income were available. When an institution has relatively ample fellowship funds, as the California Institute of Technology has, it can restrict outside work without forcing some of the most able students to abandon their studies. Where fellowship funds are relatively scarce, outside employment policies are generally less rigid.

A second policy approach is based on the assumption that a graduate student who does not have enough money to finance his education should be free to work a full week and to prolong the period of his graduate education if he so desires. The University of Minnesota Department of Aeronautical Engineering has a set of rules illustrating this approach. In 1954, 40 students in the department were enrolled for an M.S. degree and 5 for a Ph.D. degree in aeronautical engineering. Of this group of 45, about 30 students had full-time jobs on contracts. They attended six lectures a week. Under this schedule they could secure an M.S. degree in two years and a Ph.D. degree in about four and a half years. Their income from the contracts paid their tuition and living expenses. The students were required to repay the six hours they spent in lecture classes by working over the weekends and on holidays. It was reported that if it were not for federal funds, these 30 students would have had to drop out.

A third policy approach is based on the assumption that the university should view graduate students as hired labor on research contracts without regard to their status as graduate students. At least one university engineering center hires both graduate and undergraduate students on federal research contracts on this basis, and the university places no restrictions on the work load students can take on. Such a policy avoids any possibility that a university could be using federal research funds as a disguised subsidy to students. It also appears to assume that neither the university as a whole nor any of its departments has a responsibility to guide students.

University policies range with numerous variations between the extremes set by the first and third approaches. When the problem is viewed solely as one of creating the ideal environment for learning, the fewer distractions there are from study the better. A fellowship is clearly a desirable means of providing money to very able students. Universities which place strict limits on the time students can spend earning money as a means of reducing distractions from academic work are generally those with large fellowship funds.

Universities which do not have adequate fellowship funds face the dilemma of refusing to admit potentially outstanding graduate students who must spend substantial amounts of time earning money or of admitting these students with the knowledge that they may overburden themselves or fail to progress satisfactorily with their studies.

Net effect on graduate training

The importance of the effect of federal research funds on the quality of graduate training is matched by the difficulty of securing a reliable assessment of the effects. I approached the problem in two ways. First, I talked with a large number of university teachers and administrative people. Second, in view of the unsatisfactory state of knowledge on the subject, I resorted reluctantly to the distribution of a questionnaire on the subject in January 1957 (Appendix, Section 2). This was done less in the hope of securing completely objective and statistically reliable data, than in the belief that the judgments of deans and department heads were probably as good as any other measure of change in the quality of graduate training. The answers undoubtedly reflect personal biases, incomplete information, and so forth. I weighed the advisability of asking people about the quality of teaching in their own departments as opposed to asking about the country as a whole. There is probably some tendency for faculty members to view the quality of teaching in their schools and departments brightly. On the other hand, no one really knows what has happened to the quality of graduate training in his field for the country as a whole. I chose to put my trust in the ignorance imposed by lack of knowledge rather than bias generated by self-esteem. Even though the responses may miss the truth in some respects, no other measure seemed more revealing and reliable.

The deans of 31 graduate schools and 100 heads of departments of physics, psychology, bacteriology, engineering, chemistry (including biochemistry), mathematics, geology, and biology replied to the questionnaire. About 70 percent of the questionnaires distributed were returned, that is, 131 of the 191 questionnaires distributed. The returns appeared to be random. The counts which follow must therefore be taken not as precise quantities, but as rough measures of attitudes. Seventy-one percent of the respondents (deans plus department heads) stated that the average quality of training received by graduate students had improved over the decade 1948–1957 (Table A–17). Almost a quarter of the respondents said that the quality of training has not only increased but increased markedly. No respondent said that the quality of training had decreased markedly.

The judgments of groups of department heads on changes in the quality of training varied widely. Between 20 and 25 percent of the heads of departments of chemistry, biology, and bacteriology said the quality of training had declined. On the other hand, no department heads in engineering, mathematics, geology, and psychology said that the quality of training in their fields had declined.

More important to the issue at hand, what effect have federal funds had on these changes?

Take first the 71 percent who stated that the quality of training has improved. Practically all of them (62 percent of the 131 respondents) said that the federal research funds were responsible, partially or primarily, for the improvement. Within this group, 10 people (7 percent of the respondents) thought that the caliber of training had increased markedly and that the federal funds were primarily responsible. This group consisted of seven department heads and three deans. All three deans are deans of graduate study in state universities of moderate size: Florida, Louisiana, and Utah. The department heads, five of whom are heads of departments in large universities granting more than 200 Ph.D.

degrees in 1954–55, were distributed as follows: chemistry, Arkansas; chemistry, Louisville; physics, Purdue; bacteriology, Texas; physics, Washington; geology, Wisconsin; engineering, Stanford.

Next to be considered are the 17 respondents (13 percent of the total) who thought the caliber of graduate training had not changed over the period 1948–1957. Of this group, 12 did not express any opinion as to the effect of the federal funds, and it is reasonable to assume that the group as a whole thought the federal funds had had no significant effects.

Finally, there is the group of 15 respondents (11 percent of the total) who expressed the opinion that the quality of training had declined somewhat. Of these, 12 were department heads and 3 were deans. Among this group, 8 department heads (6 percent of the respondents) said that the Federal funds were primarily or partially responsible for the decline.[6] Of the 12 department heads who thought that the caliber of instruction had declined 6 were heads of departments of chemistry, 4 were heads of departments of physics, and 2 were heads of departments of bacteriology. All but 3 of the 12 were heads of departments in large universities granting more than 200 Ph.D. degrees in 1954–55.

Since the quality of training of the exceptional students is a matter of great importance, this question was asked: "As contrasted with all students, how have federal research funds affected the quality of the training of the few students potentially capable of highly creative, profound work of the highest caliber in your field?" Fifty-five percent of the respondents said that the federal research funds affected the training of such gifted students more favorably than that of all other students, while 40 percent said that all students, including the gifted ones, were affected the same way. Only 5 percent said that gifted students were adversely affected by the federal funds, as compared with all other students. But even among this 5 percent, half thought that the quality of training of all students had been improved slightly or markedly by the federal funds.

In short, among the group who answered the questionnaire, the widely publicized apprehension over the quality of training available to the exceptionally gifted graduate student was almost negligible. Indeed a majority of the respondents felt that the training of highly gifted graduate students was more favorably affected by federal research funds than was the case for other graduate students.

Respondents were asked to assess a number of the effects of federal research funds that might bear upon the quality of graduate training (Table 11). One pervasive effect of federal research funds in universities has been to increase the volume, variety, and quality of research equipment. (The responses relating to the quality and availability of faculty for teaching are discussed in the following chapter.) As a result, the typical postwar graduate student in the physical sciences and engineering is well trained in the construction, operation, foibles, and limitations of instruments.

Table 11. Percentage distribution of effects of federal funds on graduate training

| | Percent of respondents reporting — | | |
Factor	Favorable effect	No effect	Adverse effect
Availability of instruments	91	9	0
Availability of data for teaching and theses	67	27	6
Availability of faculty	57	25	18
Absorption of students in training	51	39	10
Total supply of university teachers	50	25	25
Breadth and duration of training in fundamentals	42	49	9
Capacity of individual faculty members	39	45	16

Source: Responses to questionnaire presented in Appendix, Section 2.

The other side of this coin is the query, whether the availability of instruments for production and analysis of data has led to excessive concentration on the collecting of facts and inadequate reflection on the meaning of and relations among sets of facts. Some professors and students probably incline toward data collection with relatively little concern over the meaning of the data. However, only 9 percent of the respondents thought that the breadth and duration of training in fundamentals had been adversely affected by the federal funds, while 42 percent thought that training in fundamentals had been favorably affected. Moreover, only 10 percent of the respondents thought that the federal funds had caused students to be less absorbed in their training, while 51 percent thought that the result was more complete absorption.

Graduate Study

As was pointed out in Chapter 4, federal research funds have undoubtedly inclined graduate students toward areas of work supported by the federal government and toward professors whose work is abundantly supported. Such shifts are in themselves neither good nor bad. An assessment of the effects of such "biasing" must rest on other factors. One of the most significant of these is the quality of research conducted by faculty members. If a graduate student's faculty adviser is himself engaged in work of high caliber, the graduate student is likely to benefit. To secure a general assessment of this effect, the 100 department heads gave their judgments on the effect of federal research funds on the quality of research in their fields (Table 12).

Table 12. Percentage distribution of effects of federal funds on quality of research

| Field | Percent of respondents reporting — | | | | |
| | Increase | | | No effect | Moderate decrease |
	Total	Marked	Moderate		
Total	70	20	50	20	10
Physics	80	30	50	10	10
Chemistry	50	25	25	25	25
Psychology	85	15	70	15	0
Mathematics	65	0	65	35	0
Bacteriology	90	25	65	10	0
Geology	100	25	75	0	0
Engineering	65	15	50	35	0
Biology	85	10	75	0	15

Source: Responses to questionnaire presented in Appendix, Section 2.

In summary, 70 percent of the department heads said that the federal funds have increased the quality of work in their fields either moderately or markedly. Twenty percent believe that the funds have had no effect and only 10 percent believe that the federal funds have moderately decreased the caliber of research. This means that federal research funds have not generally caused students to be engaged in routine data collection, testing, and similar chores. The federal funds are, by and large, a means of exposing them to, and of helping them to participate in, a disciplined search for more general knowledge. It should be noted, however, that while almost all department heads in most fields report no decline in the quality of research, 25 percent of the heads of departments of chemistry believe the federal funds have adversely affected the quality of research in chemistry.

The potential threat to the quality of graduate training seen by many in the first years of large-scale federal support of research has not been realized. Graduate education in the physical and biological sciences and in engineering is more rigorous than ever before, and this is attributable in part to the federal research funds. The gifted graduate student, as well as the group as a whole, is better trained.

8

Faculty and Teaching

Federal research funds have increased the demand for teachers in the physical sciences and engineering, causing shortages, disruptive differences in salary levels, and extensive use of part-time teachers. They have probably increased the emphasis placed upon research rather than teaching ability as a factor in promotions. Research grants and contracts are a source of income for many faculty members, and this raises questions as to the loyalties and values of faculty members. Finally, some universities conduct so much research with federal funds that they hire large numbers of scientists solely to do research, and fundamental questions as to the role of the university are thereby generated.

The faculty base

The total burden of teaching and research in the physical sciences, life sciences, agricultural sciences, psychology and social sciences in the universities and colleges of this country is borne by about 65,000 full-time and part-time faculty members.[1] There are the equivalent of about 60,000 full-time faculty members in these fields. About a third of the time of faculty members in these fields is spent in research.

As might be surmised from the concentration of research expenditures, the faculty members engaged in research are highly concentrated. Well over 95 percent of the faculty engaged in research are located in 180 large institutions.

Salaries and shortages

Many universities have money to hire, at the prevailing academic salaries, more qualified teachers than are now available to fill the jobs. In the academic year 1955–56, for example, about three quarters of all colleges and universities had shortages of faculty in the physical sciences.[2]

Probably the most serious shortages are found in medical schools. In the academic year 1957–58, there were 619 budgeted unfilled full-time faculty positions in the medical schools of the United States. Of them 115 were full professorships. The American Medical Association commented in the November 1958 number of its *Journal*: "This increase of approximately 90% of such vacancies in a single year represents a problem of major concern to medical education. Unless the trend is reversed, it may jeopardize certain aspects of medical education, research and care in the period that lies ahead."[3] This situation will no doubt continue to get worse before it gets better.

With few exceptions, colleges and universities have incomes forcing them to pay poor salaries to teachers. In 1957–58, the full professors in state universities were paid a median salary of $9,000, and the full professors in a private college with enrollment over 1,000 were paid a median salary of $7,000;[4] the salaries are in inflated dollars.

While the general financial position of universities is the basic explanation for the salary situation and for shortages of teachers, the federal research funds have exerted both helpful and harmful influences. They have expanded research opportunities and helped to raise salary levels. On the other hand, they have adversely affected universities since federal research funds for nonacademic laboratories have tended to draw academic people into industry. The federal government provides almost half of all industrial research and development expenditures. Almost 90 percent of the $1.8 billion spent by the aircraft industry and 60 percent of the $.7 billion spent by the electrical industry on research and development in 1956 came from federal funds.[5]

The salaries paid by private nonacademic research organizations — research centers as well as industrial concerns — are set in

142

a free market. As the National Education Association has pointed out, "competition in the open occupational market is the dominating factor, and it is in the fields of greatest shortage that the colleges suffer the most obvious handicap." [6] Salaries are bid up, with no control other than that of the free market, by private industry with federal research funds. The universities cannot use federal funds to establish salary scales competitive with private industry. As a result, there is a distressing loss of faculty to industry.

The use of federal funds to pay relatively high industrial research salaries has some ironic consequences. Low salaries — low not only in relation to industrial scales, but also in relation to the income of skilled artisans — force the wives and children of many faculty members to lead a mean existence. In this connection, a perceptive psychiatrist has noted:

> A day in the laboratory is the same for a rich scientist or a poor one, while the price of poverty will be paid by his family at home. The young scientist does not accept the full import of the fact that his wife and his youngsters are the ones who will have to spend 24 hours a day in quarters so crowded that they will lack space for peaceful family living and the dignity of privacy. [7]

The wives and children of underpaid faculty members are subsidizing an activity essential to the growth of our economy and our national existence. At the same time, the federal government provides money to private profit making concerns with which they finance an upward salary spiral to secure the people — many from universities — required to do the government work. This is a senseless situation.

Another adverse consequence of low salaries and the shortage of teachers has been increasing dependence upon part-time teachers, particularly in private universities which employ 48 percent of all part-time, but only 15 percent of all full-time teachers. The significance of part-time teachers for undergraduate instruction is indicated by the fact that there were only 16,000 full-time instructors in the school year 1955–56 in all types of institutions of higher education. In contrast, there were approximately 20,000 full professors, 18,000 associate professors, and 27,000 assistant professors.

It is possible to operate the system with fewer instructors than teachers of other faculty ranks only because colleges and universities employ about 30,000 part-time teachers. Not all part-time teachers are graduate teaching assistants, but all of the graduate teaching assistants are in the part-time group. "Without doubt, the presence of graduate students (and their spouses) provides a reservoir from which many part-time teachers come. Probably about 7,000 graduate teaching assistants in 1955–56 were part-time instructors." [8] In the face of this need, the federal research funds have, as pointed out in the Chapter 7, made it more difficult for universities to secure an adequate number of well-qualified teaching assistants and have in this manner complicated the staffing problems of universities.

I asked 131 deans and department heads whether the federal funds have been a net advantage or disadvantage to universities in securing and retaining faculty (Appendix, Section 2). Half of the respondents thought that the federal funds had resulted in a net increase in the number and quality of faculty and another 25 percent thought the funds had had no effect. However, the remaining 25 percent thought that the federal funds had adversely affected the training of graduate students through loss of faculty members to nonacademic research organizations. In some fields — mathematics, bacteriology, geology, and biology — between 35 and 50 percent of the respondents reported a net loss of faculty as a result of competition.

On balance, it seems that federal funds have helped universities to obtain and keep teachers, but in some fields of study in some universities the money has been more of a curse than a blessing.

Apart from the nonacademic competition, universities compete among themselves for faculty members. Concealed and open salary inducements, and other inducements, are frequently offered by universities to attract faculty in the sciences and engineering. Indirectly, the federal research funds are an important factor in enabling universities to bid up salaries. By and large, the effect has been to increase the bargaining power of the large state universities in their competition with private universities. The net effect of this competition is probably good, even though it is somewhat disruptive, because it tends to raise all academic salaries.

Colleges and universities also compete for faculty. A $2,000 salary differential between colleges and universities, based on published schedules, was noted above. In addition, many universities offer a higher rank than indicated by their published salary schedules, and higher beginning salaries than indicated by schedules. When 351 institutions were asked in 1957 to indicate fields in which such inducements were offered, they mentioned science, mathematics, and engineering 243 times. They mentioned all other fields combined only 122 times. Nevertheless, federal research funds probably do not cause many teachers in private colleges to shift to universities. In reporting on a series of conferences on the question of research in colleges, the National Science Foundation noted that the smaller colleges did not think that loss of faculty to universities was an important issue.[9]

Research, teaching, and promotion

The federal funds have probably increased the importance of research as contrasted with teaching in connection with decisions to hire or promote faculty members. As an experienced foundation officer has noted: "Spare time spent in research leads to prestige, promotions, and other career gains, while time spent in improving one's teaching offers no equivalent rewards." [10] Another competent observer has noted that: "With the known difficulties in evaluating the individual's performance in teaching, his contribution in research (i.e. publications) tends to take precedence in matters of his appointment, retention, and promotion." [11]

Assuming this description to be accurate, is the situation good or bad? To the extent that the major function of universities is to serve as the means of extending universal education beyond high school, teaching rather than scholarly work should predominate. But if the primary function of the university is to serve as the site for rigorous training of intelligent students and as the site for free scholarship, then competence in research should be an important prerequisite for promotion.

The tradition of rigorous training in an atmosphere of scholarship is the function less congenial to our culture. It needs protection and cultivation. Therefore, if the federal research funds have

145

increased the emphasis on research productivity in assessing faculty members, the effect is salutary.

But while research competence is important and should be rewarded, it is clearly unhealthy for the competence to be attained at the cost of a decline in the quality of undergraduate education. President Goheen of Princeton recently called attention to this problem, stressing the significance of special research inducements:

A disturbing tendency appears to be growing among a number of major universities. This is to offer a faculty member for whom one or more institutions are competing either a drastically reduced teaching schedule or an appointment for research alone. It is obvious that if this practice develops much further, many of the most able and inspiring of this country's professors may be entirely removed from undergraduate teaching at the very time that teaching talent of high competence is in short supply. From the standpoint of the individual professor, the prospect of completely free time for scholarship, research, and writing is often tempting indeed. From the standpoint of the education of students, particularly of undergraduates, the prospect of an expansion of this practice is disheartening.[12]

Federal research funds are largely responsible for making such offers possible.

In connection with selection of faculty, a person who has attracted a large volume of financial support for his research is often considered a financial asset. This is often true even though acceptance of a research grant or contract imposes a cost upon the university, either because the costs go unrecognized or because the university, school, or department wants the prestige associated with a large research enterprise. In this situation, the choice of a new faculty member can be strongly influenced by the volume of research funds which a man can bring with him. When a university keeps a man it wishes to replace or engages a new faculty member because of federal research funds, it has to a degree relinquished freedom to select teachers and investigators. Similarly, individuals lose a degree of freedom if they feel impelled to seek larger sums that are needed for the most effective prosecution of their work.

Federal funds are generally not, however, the ultimate cause of what appear to be ill-considered personnel decisions. Some universities know what they should do, but, like Liza's father in

Shaw's *Pygmalion*, "can't affort middle-class morality." The root of the problem is insufficient free funds for the general operation of the universities. If the money were there, the need to temper personnel decisions to protect or improve the financial position of the university would not arise.

Salaries from federal research funds

Most universities have a firm rule, based upon perceived dangers, against payment of all or even part of the salary of faculty members from federal research funds. These universities feel that a faculty member whose salary is paid by a federal agency could have obligations and loyalties running counter to the best interests of the universities. They also believe that they might find themselves under heavy pressure to sustain the volume of contracts, regardless of the nature of the work, in order to secure money to pay faculty salaries. Finally, they fear that widespread payment of the salaries of tenure faculty members from contract research funds might well lead the government to examine and to set rules on salary levels.

But even among universities which are scrupulous in avoiding payment of tenure faculty members from federal research funds, care must be exercised lest the problem arise as a consequence of leaves of absence. Many faculty members go on leaves of absence, while retaining their university tenure status, to work on federal contracts or to take a federal job. An administrator in one large university reported to me that the simultaneous return of all tenure faculty members on such leave without pay to work on research for the government would be the equivalent of a 10-percent increase in total salary costs in the engineering and physical science departments. The university would not have the necessary funds. This possibility has forced a number of universities to review centrally all requests for such leave and to set limits on the number of faculty members who may have leave at any one time.

In spite of these clear dangers, federal research funds are the source of the salaries of some faculty members. A few universities use contract funds to pay tenure faculty members working full-time on classified research. This policy is adopted because the universities wish the faculty members to be clearly separated from

147

the university and teaching responsibilities while they are engaged in classified research, and because they are rendering no service to the university while they work full-time on classified research. This is a logical, defensible course, clearly distinguishable from a policy which transfers a normal university salary obligation to the federal government.

Payment of part of the salary of medical school faculty members from federal research funds is a common practice, particularly at levels below the full professorial rank. In one university, not to be identified, 25 percent of the instructional engineering staff with tenure are paid from federal research contracts. From 50 to 100 percent of the tenure staff in special research organizations associated with the university are paid from federal funds. At another university, tenure professors working on federal research contracts are not only paid from federal research contracts, but paid a 25-percent bonus. The university pays from 75 to 100 percent of the 125-percent total. The entire physics faculty is paid the 25-percent bonus. The purpose of this arrangement is to attract and keep faculty. In the opinion of administrators at this university, half of the faculty in the physical sciences and engineering would leave if federal contracts were withdrawn.

In view of the clear dangers involved in payment of salaries of faculty members — particularly those with tenure — from federal research funds, why do some universities follow this practice? One reason frequently advanced is that any faculty member who is engaged primarily in the direction or conduct of research for the federal government should be paid by the government. When a faculty member spends most of his time "running a federal research project," however, the most important question to answer seems to be not who should pay the man but whether the research belongs in the university environment at all. The real explanation seems to lie in a combination of desperate financial circumstances, the need to offer financial bonuses to compensate for the absence of other attractions, and simple expediency.

The potential dangers to universities involved in the payment of the salary of tenure faculty members from federal research funds have led some persons to the conclusion that the federal government should as a matter of general policy refuse to permit payment of any part of the salaries of tenure faculty members from contract and grant funds. My view is that even though payment of salaries of faculty members with tenure might be a practice dangerous to universities, the federal government should not forbid the payment of such salaries.

Supplemental faculty income

A substantial, but unknown, number of universities fix and pay the salaries of faculty members, but permit them to receive additional income derived from federal research funds.[13]

Most universities flatly forbid faculty members to earn money from federal research contracts during the academic year. (Policies differ with respect to earnings during the three-month summer vacation. Some universities permit faculty members to work on research contracts throughout the summer, but a more common practice is to limit such work to two out of the three summer months.) In some cases, however, "overtime" or other work on federal research projects is permitted during the regular school year. Other universities permit faculty members to charge fees for consultative services to faculty members who have federal research contracts, but this is generally regarded as similar to direct earnings from contract funds and as establishing undesirable relations among faculty members. Some universities which firmly restrict the income of faculty members from research contracts during the academic year permit a limited income supplement for faculty members working on classified research (the so-called Harrell formula). Finally, some universities permit limited supplemental earnings from research contracts on an emergency basis.

Several problems, either actual or potential, have led to widespread restrictions on receipt of supplemental income from federal research funds.

First, faculty members can be tempted to spend time on research not for the sake of the research but simply to earn money, a reasonable apprehension given the level of academic salaries. Second, teaching responsibilities can be slighted. Third, dissension can be created between the engineers and physical scientists to whom these opportunities to earn extra money come most frequently and the teaching staff in the social sciences and humanities, who have fewer opportunities for outside employment. In addition, those in the physical sciences whose research is not supported by federal contracts (and who therefore have no source of supplemental income) resent those who pursue essentially the same type of research under federal contracts and receive a handsome supplemental income.

Fourth, dissension can arise between the central administration of the university, department heads, and individual faculty members. Once substantial extra research contract income is translated into an expected standard of living, resentment against loss of the income can be keen and the arguments for maintenance of the custom can be as ingenious as they are spurious.

Last, and perhaps most important, the general atmosphere, the values of faculty and students, and the sense of the mission of the university are all adversely affected by permitting faculty members to earn supplemental income from federal research contracts during the academic year.

In those universities where policies and practices relating to earnings of faculty members from federal research contracts seem to be out of control, a number of factors contribute to the difficulty. The general inadequacy of university salaries is important. The situation has not changed basically in fifty years, as indicated by the startling relevance of these comments in a 1908 Carnegie Foundation report:

A large proportion of the teachers in American universities are engaged in turning to the grindstone of some outside employment with one hand while they carry on the work of the teacher with the other. Owing to the rise in the cost of living, the proportion of teachers who seek to increase their incomes in this way is very large. The method of organization of the American university also throws a large amount of executive work upon members of the faculty. For this, extra compensation is sometimes paid. Both processes cut down the opportunity for scholarly study and take away from the dignity, simplicity, and high-mindedness of the teacher's calling.[14]

The supplementing of faculty incomes from federal research funds is thus a new aspect of an old problem. The situation today is made more difficult by the declining economic status of faculty members and by practices that grew up during and after World

War II. The high-pressure research programs during the war required many university faculty members to abandon their "own" work and to work the year round on problems arising out of the war. Many universities permitted faculty members to supplement their salaries. The faculty members often shifted to the federal payroll when joining new research organizations attached to or separate from universities. At the end of the war, heavy federal research expenditures continued, and the flood of returning G.I.'s threw an unprecedented teaching load on the faculty. Meanwhile, prices were going up, and industrial jobs at high salaries were available. As a result of these circumstances, many universities felt that they had to permit faculty members to earn extra income from research contracts.

Some of the federal agencies themselves have contributed to the problem by offering bonuses to faculty members who offer to work on research contracts, sometimes without consulting university authorities. The National Science Foundation has analyzed this practice:

Federal financing of bonuses or increments above and beyond established institutional schedules is unhealthy for both the institutions and the Federal agencies, and bilateral negotiation with respect to reimbursable salaries between faculty members and Federal agencies, by-passing department heads and the head of the institution, obviously tends to undermine orderly college and university administration.[15]

The final factor that has gotten some universities into difficulty has been purely administrative — failure to recognize the potential dangers of supplemental income and to set adequate policies before the situation got out of hand. As an example of such a situation, the vice-president of a university where the central administration was concerned over the earnings of faculty members remarked to me that the sheer size and rate of growth of contract research created a difficult problem for the university as a whole. In the year 1938–39, the university received about $200,-000 from outside sources for research. In 1955, the volume was $13 million. The university found itself with a large number of contracts which were a major influence on the institution as a whole, and without a set of general policy guides on faculty earnings and on other problems arising from the new contracts.

The potential difficulties arising from supplemental earnings can be kept from being realized if a university recognizes the danger early enough to establish firm general policies, and if it has money enough to pay adequate salaries. Most universities have established written or unwritten policies on supplemental income. The Longenecker study for the Association of American Universities includes excerpts on the supplementing of salary from the written policies of 25 universities.[16] Written policies help, but they are not the key to effective resolution of the problem. The best preventive, as is true of many problems arising out of federal research funds in universities, is spontaneous recognition by the faculty of a balance between their obligations to the university and their rights as individuals, and a common view among faculty members and the administrative staff of the university as to where this balance lies.

Inadequate university income, reflected in inadequate faculty salaries, is a problem so pervasive that the economic motive for supplemental faculty income will apparently continue well into the future.

The new class: research employees

The expansion of university research financed with federal funds has created two groups of scientists employed in various research organizations closely associated with the university, exclusive of research centers. The first group consists of younger nontenure people who are called research fellows, research associates, senior associates, or some such title, and who are employed on a probationary basis. Their salaries generally equal those paid to people with comparable backgrounds who have academic titles. After a year or two of trial, the universities generally offer academic positions to those of the group who appear most promising. This system of selecting younger faculty members is customary and predates the days of large federal research funds.

The second group of professional nontenure university employees is composed of more mature people who are employed by the university for full-time research. More than 5,000 scientists and engineers are in this group.

Employment of these people has important effects both upon

the individuals concerned and upon universities.[17] These mature professional employees lead an essentially precarious existence. Typically, they have neither academic titles nor tenure, and they do little or no teaching. Usually, their employment is limited to the duration of the research contract from which the salary is derived, but many nonfaculty professional employees shift from one contract to another and remain for years employees of the same university. They are typically compensated for this insecurity by salaries which are higher than those paid to faculty members with comparable status. Most of the nonfaculty professional employees of universities are capable teachers and investigators. Many would be welcomed as full tenure faculty members if the universities had the required funds. At the University of California at Los Angeles, for example, practically all of the professional research employees would be given faculty status if money were available. Typically, however, this group is engaged full time in research with very few teaching commitments, if any.

Many universities view the presence of a large group of nonfaculty research employees as reflecting in part their inability to secure enough money to pay salaries to a faculty of the size and kind that they desire. Generally, however, a large group of full-time university employees who do research but have no teaching responsibilities is clear evidence that the size of the research enterprise has expanded beyond that required to "enrich teaching." The university has undertaken to conduct research as research, not research integrated with the other functions of the university.

In this situation, what are the reciprocal rights and obligations of the employee and the university? Legally, it is common for the university to set up a contractual relation which makes clear that employment is only for the duration of a specified federal research contract. Morally, the situation may be somewhat different. These people are often sought out and lured into changing their employment, sometimes because they can attract research funds which the university wants. As contracts continue at a high level year after year, the nonfaculty professional group become identified with the laboratory, institute, or division of the university in which they work. They invest substantial parts of their careers in the university research program. The university

153

capitalizes on its research program as a means of securing additional funds.

A reduction of federal research grants and contracts would force many universities to fire great numbers of nonfaculty professional employees unless large amounts of money were suddenly to become available. Some universities are frank enough to say that the nonfaculty professional employee arrangement has been a prerequisite to the current scale and variety of research, and that this arrangement was planned to avoid financial embarrassment to the university in the event of a drop in the volume of federal contracts. Because of heavy reliance upon the professional nonfaculty employment relation, a number of universities with large research enterprises financed by contracts with the federal government are in a position where a sharp reduction in federal contracts would not have serious consequences for them. The universities have devised human shock absorbers.

University administrators are not ruthless, however. In interviews with the author, officials of large universities have almost invariably mentioned the obligation of the university to the employees. For example, the vice-president of a large state university said: "We are worried over the moral obligation of the university for people who have been attached to the university for years, but without faculty status. In the event of a sharp cutback in federal research funds, we would feel a strong moral obligation to help these people, but we do not know where the money would come from if the federal funds declined."

The professional nonfaculty group is a potentially rich source of teachers. With luck, a large proportion of the group might be available when the wave of increased enrollments hits universities. In the absence of such a fortunate coincidence, a marked decline in federal research grants and contracts would probably force universities to fire professional nonfaculty employees, much as the necessity for doing so would be deplored. The economic and moral problems associated with the professional nonfaculty employee are among the primary consequences of permitting university research activities to expand apart from the other functions of the university.

154

9

University Administration

The scale of federal financing of university research, the terms and conditions under which funds are made available, and the substance for the research that is financed all combine to force universities to administer research to an unprecedented degree. They must try to handle large sums of money in a businesslike way. They must try to ensure that the separate acts of a large number of individuals accustomed to a good deal of autonomy are reasonably consistent with general university policies. These new problems call for new ground rules and administrative machinery.

University research as a business operation

Federal research funds have created business and logistical problems for universities which are inherent in handling large-scale research. These problems would be difficult to solve even if the federal agencies were to administer their activities with very great skill, and the fact that they are less than perfect increases the problems.

Acceptance of contracts, even when the federal agency ostensibly pays the full cost of the research, can cost a university money. For example, a faculty member at one university was satisfied with a proposed Air Force contract for classified research which would have obligated the university to provide around-the-clock armed guards at a cost of $20,000 a year. An astronomer at another university was about to receive a grant from the National Science Foundation when the business office noted that "a small physical appendage" would be required if the work was to be done. The business office called to see what this appendage might be. It was a $30,000 addition to the observatory, cost to be borne by the university. In neither case did the university have the money to meet the commitments to be made on its behalf by the faculty members, and the federal funds had to be rejected. In a number of universities, contract negotiations with individual faculty members have resulted in the assumption of a total research program that could not be housed in existing facilities.

Some universities found in the early days of federal research grants and contracts that agencies were negotiating contracts with individual faculty members which left payment of insurance premiums, vacation provisions and similarly mundane but fiscally important matters either vague or firmly resolved in a manner unsatisfactory to the university business office. Experience has thus shown that when the volume of federal grants and contracts is large, universities must take care not to overcommit their total resources, or to incur heavy expenses inadvertently.

Universities receiving a large volume of federal research grants and contracts are faced with complex business arrangements:

> All government contracts and some grants contain requirements pertaining to purchase orders, subcontracts and prior approvals . . . The complexities of the problems pertaining to purchase orders, subcontracts and prior approvals necessitate a well-considered and well-understood procedure for handling . . . Various sections of a government contract may often contain requirements which must be included in subcontracts or purchase orders. The distinction between a subcontract and a purchase order is often of prime importance in order to determine what terms and conditions must be included . . . Any substantial volume of government owned property in the custody of an educational institution requires a well-planned and administered system of property accounting. This is necessary to comply with the contractual conditions and to avoid confusion at the time of government inspection and audit of property . . . Legal or administrative requirements covering government cost-reimbursement contracts specify that the records be preserved and made available for a period of at least six years from the date of the final invoice or voucher submitted under the contract . . . If no provision for termination is included in the contract or grant, the institution's rights to recovery of costs which have been incurred but not reimbursed, or which are necessary for the settlement of outstanding commitments, generally will be subject to common law and equity.[1]

156

In a large university, hundreds of federal research grants and contracts, requiring negotiations with each of the major federal agencies which contracts for research, are involved. Each contract and grant must be handled individually. Each must be scrutinized to protect the interests of the university. The whole package must be examined in the light of effects on schools, on departments, and on the university as a whole. Accounts must be kept in a form that will make available the required information.

These tasks, routine for the most part, are nevertheless important. Taking advantage of quantity discounts and discounts for prompt payment of invoices, for example, can save substantial sums. Ignorance of the operations of faculty members which lead to expenditures not authorized by the terms of contracts can result in disallowance by federal auditors and a cash outlay by the university.

Federal rules

The minimum array of administrative chores created for a university by acceptance of federal research contracts is enlarged by a number of practices of federal agencies, some required by law, some by regulation, and still others by practices required by neither law nor regulation.

The most prolific source of administrative difficulty has been the application of procedures for procurement of tangible goods to the quite different problems involved in purchasing research. These difficulties are most often associated with research contracts rather than research grants, but the legal form is not fundamentally important. The key consideration is the extent to which federal agencies purchasing research use the regulations, contract forms, auditing procedures, organization, and personnel which are used in procuring hardware. The greater the degree to which standard procurement procedures and organizations are applied to research, the greater the administrative difficulties.

As Director of the Office of Scientific Research and Development, Dr. Vannevar Bush foresaw precisely the problems which would arise if the procurement type of contract were used for research:

Since research does not fall within the category of normal commercial or procurement operations which are easily covered by the usual contractual relations, it is essential that certain statutory and regulatory fiscal requirements be waived in the case of research contractors . . . . Adherence to the usual procedures in the case of research contracts will impair the efficiency of research operations and will needlessly increase the cost of the work to the Government . . . Colleges and universities in which research will be conducted . . . are, unlike commercial institutions, not equipped to handle the detailed vouchering procedures and auditing technicalities which are required of the usual Government contractors.[2]

This advice was taken to heart by the War Department. In 1946, President Eisenhower, then Chief of Staff of the Army, sent a memorandum to chiefs of general and staff divisions and to the generals of the major commands, stating that "we must separate responsibility for research and development from the functions of procurement, purchase, storage and distribution."[3] But as is often the case with positive policy pronouncements at a high level, even in a military organization, it is one thing to give an order and another to have it carried out. Eight years after the statement of War Department policy, the Executive Officer of the Office of the Chief of Research and Development of the Department of the Army told a congressional committee: "We hope to get eventually a separate set of procurement regulations which would permit us contracting for research under special regulations drawn up for that purpose alone and not tied up to procurement, and it will be a major step forward, I am certain."[4]

The fact that the Department of Defense as a whole has not established a research contract system adjusted to the needs of university research has caused the difficulties to persist. Much of the work of the procurement officers of that Department is with industrial concerns which supply goods and equipment. The procurement people are well trained, as they should be, to protect the government by vigilant efforts to secure compliance with the letter of procurement contracts. When such persons apply to research in universities procedures devised for purchase of hardware from profit-making concerns, there is a high probability of incompatibility. Typically, difficulties are more likely to occur during the period when a federal agency first establishes relations with universities in the research field, and the difficulties are more likely to persist if decentralized procurement offices are the points of contact between the federal agency and universities. In fact, it is quite possible for the central research organization of a federal agency to have a set of operating policies and procedures that is satisfactory to universities and at the same time have local procurement people at loggerheads with university administrators and scientists.[5]

Apart from the inappropriate application of procurement procedures to research, the common practice of keeping title to research equipment provided to universities in the hands of federal agencies created, in the words of the National Science Foundation, "one of the most troublesome administrative problems involved in the federal support of research at colleges and universities . . ."[6] The difficulties arose from record-keeping and the fact that most of the equipment was obsolescent or cannibalized by the time the university finished with it. This problem was, however, resolved in 1958 by the passage of an act (S.4039) which gave agencies making contracts or grants authority to give universities title to equipment purchased with research grant or contract funds.

Business administration for research

Universities organize for the business aspect of research dealings with the federal government in two general ways. The first pattern might be called a convergent form of organization, typically involving expansion of the existing central university business or treasurer's office. The second might be called a divergent form of organization, involving the establishment of "institutes," "divisions," or "departments" not only to handle business operations but also to coordinate university research and to promote research.

The convergent form of organization does not require extensive discussion, since it involves little or nothing in the way of administrative superstructure, although the existing business offices may be substantially expanded. Quite typically the convergent form of organization reflects a university policy of avoiding overt or intensive soliciting of research.

The divergent form of organization typically reflects a university environment in which positive efforts are made to expand research in terms of dollar expenditures and staff. Often, although

159

not invariably, the administrative research institutes cover the engineering but not the physical science departments of the university, usually because engineering departments have had closer contacts with industry. Some research institutes that are now large recipients of federal research funds were originally established in conjunction with engineering departments to promote and coordinate industrial consulting, testing, and applied research.[7]

A number of universities have gone a step farther by setting up nonprofit corporations as distinct entities to handle contracts for their faculty members and to promote and administer the business side of research contracts. The incorporated type of organization for research administration is found, for example, at the Georgia Institute of Technology, the University of Kansas, the Agricultural and Mechanical College of Texas, Ohio State University, and the University of Louisville. The statement of functions of the Ohio State organization is typical:

> The Ohio State University Research Foundation is a nonprofit organization, incorporated separately from the University but closely affiliated therewith. The Foundation negotiates for and administers research projects sponsored by industry and government and carried out in the University laboratories under faculty supervision. Only projects of significant value to graduate education in furtherance of the University's prime objectives are accepted.[8]

There are some noteworthy differences between these separately incorporated organizations, particularly those attached to state universities, and the unincorporated administrative research institutes. The device of incorporation is a means of insulating all financial matters having to do with research from the review, inspection, influence, and control of state legislatures or other state bodies. The foundation, not the university, is the contracting party. All income, including indirect-cost receipts, is foundation and not university income. The separately incorporated research foundation device invented by state universities is in some respects analogous to the research center device, discussed in Chapter 10. The first is a means of circumventing state administrative and statutory controls that are felt to encumber the administration of research. The second is a means of circumventing federal controls.

Whether it is wise for universities to establish special organizations to handle the business aspects of research and to solicit research is debatable. A case can be made for putting these functions in a special organization. The tasks are quite specialized, and they may be performed more effectively if the people who perform them are placed in special organizations. Moreover, these special tasks often involve an element of salesmanship, customer contact work, and self-advertisement that may be uncongenial to faculty members or to those engaged in academic administration. Finally, a well-directed institute can serve a solidly useful academic function by undertaking to make research of maximum value to the teaching of faculty and to the learning of graduate students. It can instill a point of view and serve as a stimulating influence.

But the establishment of a separate, divergent institute for the administration of research also creates potential dangers, as a study for the American Council on Education has pointed out:

Staff members are involved in serving two masters — the regular department and the research department. There is a tendency for the research department to involve the institution in research not of interest to the regular academic departments. There is also a tendency to establish a duplicate business organization. The argument that research involving several academic departments requires the creation of a separate research department can be answered equally well through the establishment of interdepartmental management committees.[9]

Even more significant is the possibility that research may tend to become an end in itself, unrelated to the mission of the university. Special research organizations may pursue research without regard to the balance among functions of the university of which they are a part. This is particularly true of the separately incorporated research foundations. If a separately incorporated research foundation acts too independently, it can become a power in its own right. It can exert a strong influence on the kinds of research undertaken by the faculty. It can stand as a wedge between the faculty and the university administration on general university research policies. "In addition, there are the added burdens of much more formal, legal, contractual, and operating relationships between the foundation and the institution." One not entirely disinterested observer, the general manager of a commercial testing laboratory, has expressed a skeptical view of the activities of research "institutes" associated with universities:

> Collectively our educational institutions are spending hundreds of thousands of dollars each year in the preparation, printing, and distributing of expensively illustrated brochures, pamphlets, booklets, and other advertising propaganda for the soliciting of purely commercial work from industry . . . This is pure commercial high-pressure selling and using the name of the institution and its educational prestige for the sordid purpose of disguising ordinary commercial work as 'scientific research' in an endeavor to justify its being placed at a University . . . As an adjunct to education, the research work at universities should be on a proper plane and in proper proportion. When the research activities become the dominant activities and interest of a major part of the faculty and thus interfere with the educational activities the so-called adjunct has grown from a benign to a malignant tumor.[10]

To indicate that despite its bias this view is not entirely without substance, I quote from Harry H. Goode, Professor of Electrical Engineering, Director of the Willow Run Research Center, and Assistant Director of the Engineering Research Center of the University of Michigan:

> The type of work engaged upon through the Engineering Research Institute of the University of Michigan runs the whole gamut from problems which are very fundamental in nature to those which are purely testing in character . . . We are, however, in direct competition with research agencies, such as Mellon, Battelle, and Armour Institutes, as well as foundations and organizations such as our own in various universities and colleges . . . In addition to the faculty, we employ a staff of full time professional people . . .
> The solicitation or procurement of research involves advertising. Some of my colleagues shudder when I come right out and call it that . . . We encourage our staff to present papers before the various technical societies, and we often purchase and distribute reprints of such papers . . . Finally, the two assistants to the director are expected to get out and contact, in one case, the industries, and, in the other, the Government agencies, so as to bring our services continuously to their attention.[13]

This philosophy is a clear and consistent statement of a point of view shared by a substantial number of faculty members in other universities. This point of view represents the institutionalization of the individual faculty member who engages in outside consulting work to a degree and under conditions which bring into question the balance of his loyalties to the university and to those from whom he earns outside income.

When the values and objectives of a special research organization differ from those of the university of which it is a part, the engineering of a change in philosophy, values, and loyalties by a dean or a president is most difficult, primarily because loss of income by faculty members is involved.

In some large universities, the problems created by special organizations for solicitation and business management of research contracts appear to be less the result of a form of organization than of failure to establish and sustain a clear, generally accepted notion of the central missions of the university and of the outer limits of its activities.

Substantive review of research

Policy questions of great importance to the university as an institution and to the faculty as a group are involved in the acceptance of federal research funds by individual faculty members:

Should faculty members accept classified research?

Should the research accepted by faculty members be limited to the volume and kind of research required to enhance teaching?

Should new organizations for research be set up within the university, or should research be contained within the existing academic departments?

How much time should faculty members spend on federally financed research, and what effect should such work have on their incomes?

A university ignores such questions only at its peril, for there is no assurance that the independent decisions of faculty members, departments, or even schools will yield a result acceptable to the faculty as a whole. A high degree of departmental autonomy is obviously necessary. On the other hand, it is equally obvious that federal research funds force the adoption of some general policies which must be observed by individual faculty members regardless of their personal preferences.

The ideal situation is one in which there is agreement among the faculty, the president, his staff, and the regents or trustees. Obviously, if a clear consensus exists concerning the kinds of work that should be performed, no central review of the substance of research grants and contracts would be required.

This consensus does not always exist, however. When, for example, a faculty member of one university wanted to undertake some theoretical work on rocket propellants under a contract that would have required him to submit all findings to the Navy and to give the Navy priority in publication, the university advised that the contract be turned down. At another university, the department of economics was about to sign a contract for a routine economic survey of a state as a service to the state government when the staff of the office of the president inquired whether the department felt that this kind of work represented the best investment of time. The contract was turned down.

The problems of university policy generated by acceptance of federal research funds are so extensive and important that in most universities the substance of proposed research is reviewed. This review may consist of a purely *pro forma* look at a proposed contract or grant proposal by the department chairman, but generally, the substance of the proposed research is formally reviewed at successive levels in the academic hierarchy.

In some universities, the formal review is by faculty members. The California Institute of Technology, for example, has a contracts committee composed of faculty members who review and recommend contract proposals to the President on the basis of scientific desirability. Princeton University has a faculty Board of Scientific and Engineering Research responsible for all outside sponsored research, including administration of the university patent policy. Since the major objective of the review process is, or should be, to speed the attainment of a faculty consensus, there is much to be said for leaving the review in the hands of a faculty group. If the process works well, the number and proportion of contract proposals which the faculty committee must question or reject on substantive grounds tends to decline as the period of experience in dealing with contract problems lengthens and a stronger faculty consensus is built.

Many universities leave central review of research proposals to administrative officials, individually or in groups, rather than to a faculty group. For example, at the Massachusetts Institute of Technology, the Director of the Division of Industrial Cooperation and the appropriate dean must approve contracts. As another example, the Board of Regents of the University of California must approve all contracts. In practice the staff of the President's office reviews grant and contract proposals for the regents. This staff checks the substance of research quite carefully and frequently raises questions. The staff is rarely overruled by the regents.

Review of the substance of research proposals by the administrative staff sometimes reflects the absence of agreement between the faculty and the administration on the general policies which should govern acceptance of federal research funds. The further the faculty and the administration of a university are from a working agreement, the more elaborate the machinery is likely to be. Size has a tendency to give rise to elaborate procedures and controls by hampering the attainment of consensus. Whether such elaborate rules are necessary or simply a response to an urge to administer is debatable. As might be expected, administration generally takes the former view and faculty members the latter.

In summary, the strength of the faculty consensus on major research policy questions, the degree to which this consensus is enforced by social pressures, the size of the university and the degree to which the views of faculty and administrative staff coincide influence the nature of and machinery for the review process.

Strain — administrators and faculty

A general source of strain between faculty and administrators is the tendency for persons at each level in a bureaucracy to consider themselves and those in their hierarchical class to be the level at which true wisdom and balanced perspective are concentrated.[12] That level is also often considered the one at which the really important decisions are made. This may help explain why "freedom of research" is invoked most often by persons who are authoritarian in their relations with those over whose work they have some control. Actions taken higher on the ladder are sometimes considered essentially unproductive maneuvering that can reach merely administrative or political ends. They often appear to be taken by persons whose actions are misguided or irrelevant and whose mission seems to be to impede, curb, and delay. Actions taken by those lower on the ladder are often regarded as the commendable efforts of zealots on whom the productivity of the organization depends but who simply cannot or will not understand the full range of factors that must be taken into account in making the broader decisions.

When these attitudes develop, they are generally accompanied by the attribution of somewhat stereotyped personal characteristics to those in other hierarchical classes. Those above — the business office staff or the officer responsible for university research policies — are often regarded as deficient in specialized training and viewed with a mild tolerance. Those below — the faculty — are often regarded as highly but narrowly trained and viewed somewhat paternalistically.

Another source of conflict is a tendency at times to oversimplify the distinction between scientists and administrators. There are people who do research at the bench and nothing else. They are clearly scientists and not administrators. But a large proportion of faculty members engaged directly in research are responsible in various ways and degrees for the work of others, and the discharge of these responsibilities constitutes administration. Perhaps they should not be so engaged, but unless the amount of university research is curtailed, many will continue to function as administrators. The people whose work is confined solely to such tasks as preparing budgets and processing personnel actions are clearly administrators and not scientists. When scientists or administrators overlook the fact that many people perform mixed functions, it becomes easier to sort people into "we" and "they" groups.

A strong "we" versus "they" atmosphere in a university laboratory impedes the readiness to communicate and the good working relations that are essential to effective research. If administrators view the faculty as a group apart, they may be led to see their job as an end in itself and forget that their role is to help the faculty. The large group of people who have both scientific and administrative duties may deplore and slight their administrative work because of the low esteem in which these activities are held. Faculty members may fail to appreciate the importance of decisions which affect them but which they do not make. They may therefore resent the fact that these decisions are made.

Failure to foresee the consequences of administrative decisions, and insistence upon temporizing, or even shirking of responsibility for making administrative decisions can also cause trouble. For example, administrators between the individual faculty member and the central review point — department heads, deans, and so on — prefer at times not to disturb their personal relations with faculty members by questioning or turning down research grants or contracts which they believe should not be accepted. Buck-passing at the intermediate levels often places the central review group in a difficult position. They must turn down proposals which not only have been initiated by faculty members typically jealous of their independence but approved by those in the academic hierarchy who are supposed to protect the interests of faculty members. Rejection of a contract proposal by a central review group often appears arbitrary, and the strain is increased if there is a long lapse between the time the faculty member makes the proposal and the time he hears of the rejection.

The establishment of an *ex-officio* whipping boy at the center of a large organization is a common administrative device to sustain harmony within subordinate parts by shifting the responsibility for difficult or unpleasant decisions from the subordinate executive. The function of the whipping boy is to make hard decisions. The trouble is that once people engage in a tacit conspiracy to have decisions made centrally in order to avoid unpleasantness, the process of centralization often gets out of hand. Then the evils of overcentralization of the power of decision appear to overbalance the gains achieved by shifting the power of decision to the center, and strain results.

Strain is created not only by the fact that decisions tend to be centralized when a university conducts a large volume of federal research contracts, but also by the fact that administrators rather than scholars or scientists make many central decisions. For example, in the process of keeping track of the university's financial

167

status, the business office asks questions of deans, department heads, and individual faculty members. People in the business office must say no at times to faculty members, sometimes because the academic side abdicates. On the other hand as the Director of the National Science Foundation has pointed out:

There may be a possible tendency of a strong administrative office to dominate the research program of the institution. In fact, an aggressive office is in a position to exercise pressure upon the research staff of the institution itself. Or it may tend to insulate the scientist from his opposite number in the supporting agency.[13]

Some of these administrative staffs have been aggressive and have made decisions better left to the faculty. In general, however, the federal funds have as a side effect made both administrators and faculty members aware of the inevitability of difficulties in administering large scale research, and increased their capacity to administer and their respect for each other.[14]

The universities which have resolved all of these strains best seem to recognize frankly that the problem exists, and faculty and administration both make a continuing intelligent effort to communicate problems and to deal as much as possible on a face-to-face basis.

It is likely that if research is on a small scale and there is a strong consensus among the faculty creating effective social pressures towards a commonly accepted code which is also accepted by administrators, there will be little strain.

Consideration of the manner in which standards are typically enforced in European universities strengthens this view. I have discussed the practice with about seventy-five persons in universities, ministries, and research organizations in eight countries in Western Europe. None knew of any European university where research is centrally reviewed, and most expressed surprise at the American custom.

The reasons there is no central review in Europe are for the most part the reverse of the reasons central review is common in this country. European universities are typically more homogeneous in their concept of the rights, duties, and obligations of professors. A large American university encompasses more fields, and hence, needs faculty members of wider diversity of training, attitudes, and professional experience than European universities. In addition, the academic senate of the European university with the rector as representative of the faculty is a strong force for the achievement and tacit enforcement of a meeting of minds as to the kind of work a faculty member should undertake. Professors who share the same views and attitudes often exercise strong control over the various departments. Those lower on the academic ladder are unlikely to breach the walls of academic decorum. In short, the kind and volume of research which the faculty of a European university will undertake with the aid of outside funds is not uncontrolled, but the means and process of control although exceedingly strong are neither direct nor apparent.

Since research on a small scale is felt to be appropriate to the academic environment in Europe, the university is not required to watch the effect of outside research funds as closely as in this country. To the extent that a close look at finances, space, laboratory modification, and other administrative matters is required, the detailed review of budgets and the specificity of governmental appropriations in effect perform this function. This process permits European university people to unite in castigating politicians for the kinds of decisions which in this country are made within the university.

Strain — universities and federal agencies

Given the wide differences between the objectives of federal agencies and universities and between university and government personnel, a degree of strain in working together is to be expected. Each group criticizes the way the other does business.

The universities criticize the federal rules and regulations, often with ample justification. On the other hand, they in turn have created problems by failure to understand that a new set of federal regulations and administrators could not be created overnight to meet the unique requirements of a new government-university relation, and that funds derived from taxes could not be handed over to universities with no accounting. The universities are also at times critical of the quality of the federal people with whom they must deal, and they are sometimes justified in doing so. But a more impressive aspect of the government-university relation is the emergence of a new kind of research administrator associated with both universities and government.

Critical observations by universities, it should be noted, relate to administrative matters rather than to the substance of research. The federal administrators are rarely accused of attempting to influence the substance of research. I have heard of only one instance in which a federal administrative official undertook to influence a line of investigation, and he was quickly repudiated by his superiors. The complaint of university people is not that the system results in the federal control of research, but that it makes them feel as if they were being nibbled to death by mice.

Critical comments by university people are matched by equally sharp criticism by federal administrators of the way some universities manage their affairs. The most frequent criticism of university administration is the low level of cost consciousness, the rudimentary nature of cost data, and the failure of many universities to understand the fact that large public agencies must move slowly and that they must maintain protections against misuse of public funds. Here again, however, it should be noted that one of the unintended but important effects of providing large sums of money to universities for research has been a general strengthening of the administrative capacity of universities.

In summary, given the relative newness of the research relations between federal agencies and universities and the complex problems of adjusting the ways of doing business of large bureaucracies and universities, the adaptability, forbearance and inventiveness shown by both parties are more impressive than the points of conflict.

Yet the situation is not perfect, and one is led to ask why some universities and agencies seem to handle the administrative problems easily, while others seem to be in trouble frequently.

For the federal agencies, experience indicates the following steps to improvement:

1. Keep contracts short, simple, and designed for research rather than for procurement.

2. Give universities title to research equipment.

3. Establish administration of research contracts as an administrative specialty, separate from procurement.

4. Hire good administrative people and keep them on the job so that they can gain experience and get to know the people in universities.

5. Build a good staff to work with universities on the substance of research.

The quality of the faculty of a university and of its administrative staff is the key factor in its contract relations with federal agencies. If the faculty is strong it is in a better position to choose among federal sources of funds. There is some flexibility in that a researcher may choose the agency which will support a given area of research. A strong faculty and a strong administrative staff can generally insist on suitable terms and conditions simply by refusing to sign contracts that contain unacceptable clauses.

On the other hand, if the faculty and administration are relatively weak and the faculty wishes to undertake additional contract research, their bargaining position is weak. In this circumstance, faculty members may be forced to accept contracts which are much less than ideal with respect to stability, substance, and so forth. Finally, strong rapport between the faculty and the administrative staff seems to contribute to the ability of a university to deal effectively with federal agencies on research matters. In some universities the attainment of this happy state of affairs appears to be more difficult than the establishment of a reasonable *modus vivendi* with federal agencies.

10 ←————————————————————————

University Organization

Federal research funds have by their sheer volume forced changes in the way research is organized in universities. These changes range from the working arrangements of scientists themselves to the organizational superstructures erected to contain research. The organization of research has been affected by government funds for large and complex apparatus. The funds have also made possible experimentation with various kinds of team research to cope with the limitations of the human mind in comprehending phenomena and relations progressively seen to be more complex. The massive effort to compress time by spending federal money finds expression in part in large university research organizations.

Forces from within science

In assessing the effects of research funds on the organization of university research, it is important to bear in mind the forces arising from within science that have influenced the organization of research. Among the most important of these are increasing specialization and increasing reliance upon precise measurement. Collection of the data that serve to suggest and to test hypotheses has become a task of progressively greater complexity and cost. New instruments, which are not gadgets but powerful forces for the advancement of knowledge, permit the collection of data with unprecedented speed and precision. President Stratton of the Massachusetts Institute of Technology has epitomized the changes:

The scale of research and the complexity of its techniques have grown beyond anything imagined a few decades ago . . . A change had begun to set in before the war, but it was the war that contributed principally to a major revolution in the method and spirit and scale of laboratory investigation. Two extraordinary developments have helped to bring about this transformation. The technique and instruments made available by the advancement of electronics has made its impression on every branch of physical science. These remarkable gains in our capacity to measure can be exploited only at the cost of great complexity of instrumentation. Progress in nuclear studies has been hastened by many years through the Manhattan Project and the Atomic Energy Commission. The cyclotron, the synchrotron, and now the bevatron have become indispensable tools of nuclear physics — powerful tools whose cost of construction and maintenance lie far beyond the private resources of a university. These developments in electronics and nuclear physics have set the pace in science.[1]

Similarly, the biological and social sciences rely increasingly upon collection and analysis of large volumes of data and upon greater precision of measurement.

These changes have not been "caused by" federal research funds. Most of the scientific and technological advances prerequisite to revolutionary changes in instrumentation came about independently of federal research funds. The increasing complexity and the resulting degree of specialization in science are an expression of the total development of the world of science to which the federal funds have given added momentum.

Team research

Much research in universities financed with federal funds can, partly because of the applied and developmental character of the work, be carried out effectively only by drawing together investigators with diverse training and experience. As a result, federal funds have been the primary force in an expansion of team research to dimensions unheard of before World War II. President Stratton has noted:

There was a time when scientific investigation was largely a matter of individual enterprise but the war taught scientists to work together in groups; they learned to think in terms of a common project, they were impressed by the progress to be made through unified action. A notable degree of this spirit has been transfused into the life of our larger universities and trends toward the increasingly systematic organization of research are widespread and highly significant.[1]

This expansion of team research has undoubtedly been pro-

173

ductive and, in some areas, imperative. The values of team research have been pointed out by ex-President Dodds of Princeton:

Project research often, though not always, involves team play in contrast to the individual scholar working by himself, sometimes in too lonely
grandeur, in his own ivory tower. When the team play is good, it works for
cross-fertilization and the mutual stimulation which intellectual intercourse
engenders. Young scholars find places on the teams and thus may enjoy
opportunities for intimate association with older men which might otherwise be denied them. In many cases modern research entails the collecting,
marshalling, and interpretation of masses of data beyond the capacity of a
single scholar to assemble or digest. In such situations a research team is
the natural solution.

But Mr. Dodds then proceeded to point out that the values
of team research, stimulated in large part by federal funds, have
not been secured without paying a price: "Team play . . . may
evolve into a deterrent to the cultivation of a capacity for self-
powered inquiry. Stimulation by others may easily lead one into
a state of intellectual dependence on others . . ." [2]

The present danger is not that the power of the team approach
is unappreciated, but that the importance of individuals working
alone may be underestimated. As Paul Klopsteg observed: "The
most profound of new ideas are more likely to issue from the
gifted individual with time and opportunity to think than from
the large team." [3]

In this connection, William H. Whyte has argued in *The Organization Man* that:

Group work is fashionable, and if people are franker, it is because the
climate almost compels them to be. It is not that there has been an increase
in the kind of people by nature suited to group work. The change has been
in the *environment* of research, and its molding effect has been felt by all.
The foundation, the universities, and the government have actively con-
spired to change the climate, but merely by riding with the trend, they have
created a growth that can stifle the very progress they seek.[4]

When federal research funds are distributed, there is no discrimination against the scientist who prefers to work alone. There
is plenty for all. The real danger, which cannot be ignored, is that
the indirect effect of the money, together with forces from within
science, generates an atmosphere leading fewer people to wish to
work alone.

Universities are the places in our society where the maintenance of free inquiry into the unknown by individual thinkers is a prime goal in itself. The universities, if they are to serve the unique function to which they lay claim, must serve as a counterbalance to the pull of large federal funds for research that can be performed effectively only by groups. This can be done only by preserving and fostering an atmosphere and a social climate in which the productive individual is honored and rewarded. If enough universities do this, the encouragement of team research through the availability of large sums of federal money will not be a serious problem.

University-associated research organizations

Special research organizations within universities are not new. Since the 1880's, when graduate schools began to develop in this country, the central structure of university departments has been supplemented by special organizations. These have been set up to recognize emerging fields of study, to attract donors of money, to bring a new point of view or technique to bear on a field of study, to make effective use of a physical facility such as a collection or a library, or to provide a suitable post for a faculty member. Before World War II, these institutes, centers, foundations, and laboratories were almost always closely integrated with the university. If a physical facility existed, it was usually on the campus. If the organization had a professional staff, the staff generally had faculty status and taught classes. Often graduate students worked in the supplemental organization.

During and after World War II, however, the federal government turned to universities for research tasks which could be effectively performed only by establishing a new organizational form. The following requirements evolved, and the existing university structures could meet them only partially and imperfectly:

1. Capacity to handle large, integrated research problems, such as systems of continental warning and defense, the development of an atomic bomb, and surveillance of a battlefield which might extend across continents.

2. Ability to attract people of great competence.

175

3. Performance of classified research without interfering with other missions of the university.

4. Presentation of research needs at the top of the federal structure.

5. Expeditious, effective transfer of ideas, models, and prototypes into effective industrial production and into effective use by governmental agencies.

6. Ability to move quickly and easily from one task to another and from one scale of operation to another.

7. Effective administration of large physical facilities and large numbers of employees.

8. Concentration upon research as an end in itself, not modified by the demands of teaching nor by the need to show a profit.

9. Quick response to the needs of federal agencies without direction by the agencies.

University departments met some of these needs, but the high degree of organization and direction required for some large tasks, the classified nature of the work, the sheer size of the enterprises, and the complex administrative problems were not well suited to the university environment.

Federal laboratories also met some of the needs, but recruitment and retention of personnel of high quality to work in laboratories run by the Department of Defense had been difficult. Moreover, flexibility is not a prominent characteristic of federal operations.

Similarly, industrial laboratories met some but not all of the requirements. The salary problem can be solved, and large physical facilities can be made available. In addition, industrial concerns can often provide managerial talent of high caliber for government-owned facilities. On the other hand, industrial laboratories do not provide the most effective means of transferring the product of research into production when many firms are involved. Finally, the profit motive sets limits on the flexibility with which private concerns may be used.

Since neither federal, university, nor industrial laboratories of the type existing before World War II met all of the needs generated by war and postwar requirements, a new organizational form was invented.

This new form was a research organization financed wholly by federal funds, engaged solely in research and development with a research mission set in general terms by a federal agency, but with operating responsibility and scientific direction centered in non-federal employees. Most significant, the new organizations were outside the federal structure, occupying no place on the bureaucratic hierarchical ladder and free of most of the federal regulations governing such matters as salary levels and hiring and firing.

Most of the new research organizations were attached to universities, a development accounted for largely by the way the problem of scientific mobilization for World War II was solved. (There is no inherent reason why the new research organizations should be attached to universities, and some are not. The Knolls Laboratory, for example, is managed by the General Electric Company for the Atomic Energy Commission. The Rand Corporation is an independent research corporation operated under an Air Force contract. Associated Universities, Inc. operates the AEC-owned Brookhaven Laboratories under the general guidance of nine universities. Whether the new research organization is managed by a university or by an industrial organization is of minor significance as compared with other characteristics. Brookhaven, a separately incorporated research organization, has much more in common with the Radiation Laboratory, managed by the University of California, than the Radiation Laboratory has in common with the Human Resources Research Office, a research organization managed by George Washington University.)

The essential task during the war was to organize scientists for the solution of problems of offensive and defensive warfare. Among the many difficulties faced in attaining this objective was a structural one. Most of the nation's most capable investigators in the physical and biological sciences were in a few large universities. They could be expected to work most effectively if they stayed there. Association with a university kept one important condition of work constant for a group of people who were asked to make a radical shift in the substance of their research and in their approach to research.

The nature of the tasks themselves resulted in the rapid growth of research in a few universities. Most of the scientific

177

problems related to the rapid exploitation of known scientific principles, and the exploitation could be most rapid if large groups were brought together for an organized attack on segments of a single large problem. Only large universities had the staff and the experience necessary to handle great numbers of people and large amounts of money.

This innovation was highly effective. The Los Alamos Laboratory, associated with the University of California, developed the atomic bomb. The Applied Physics Laboratory, attached to the Johns Hopkins University and financed by the Navy Department, developed the proximity fuse. The Radiation Laboratory, an interservice undertaking associated with the Massachusetts Institute of Technology, became the radar research headquarters of the nation and a major electronics center. Both the wartime success and the peacetime potentialities of this structural innovation led the Armed Forces to continue and improve the device after the war. In addition, when the civilian Atomic Energy Commission took over the nuclear research and production facilities built up by the military Manhattan District it found this kind of organization convenient.

The connection of the research organizations with the universities may be measured in various ways. The extent to which universities control the personnel policies of research organizations associated with them differs. In some associated research organizations, the university has the power to hire and fire, to promote and demote, and to fix pay scales, vacations, and other benefits. Some organizations set these policies for themselves. There are wide differences in the teaching duties of the staff of the associated research organization and in the proportion of staff members who have faculty status. Graduate students work in some associated research organizations. The financial control of the universities over the associated research organizations differ. Some organizations receive no university money. Indeed, the management of some of the organizations returns a profit to the university in the form of the difference between a management fee and the actual cost of management. Others depend quite heavily upon university support. The degree of university control over the budgets of the organizations also varies widely. Finally, and this is not a factor to be underestimated, the distance of the associated research organization from the campus varies widely.

The status and function of the associated laboratories typically change over the years, so the problems faced by universities in relation to the laboratories are continually changing. For example, the Microwave Laboratory of Stanford University has grown from a small group working on fundamental problems in electronics to a large research organization engaged in the development of highly specialized, powerful vacuum tubes and in the construction and use of a large linear accelerator. As another example, the Stanford Research Institute had a close association with the Stanford University in the years immediately after World War II, but the two organizations now have only a remote association. On the other hand, the Institute for Social Research of the University of Michigan a few years ago had little more than a geographic association with the University. Now several staff members of the institute teach, have faculty status, serve on faculty committees, and are paid by the university.

Closest to the standard departmental structure of universities is the institute or laboratory staffed by faculty members, with graduate students, and financed from both university and federal funds. These organizations are distinguished from standard departments in that they have a definite mission and a function narrower than that of a department. Some were set up before the war; others have been established after the war in response to the availability of federal funds

Somewhat more remote from the standard departmental structure is a set of associated organizations with a primary research mission, whose staff members do not have faculty status, and which are financially heavily dependent on federal research grants and contracts. These operating "research institutes," which are quite different from the institutes that are merely holding companies for research, are fairly common. The Engineering Research Institute of the University of Michigan, for example, employs scientists and engineers to conduct research. According to the By-Laws of the University of Michigan (Sec. 30.16, Regents Proceedings, 28 October 1955), the Institute "shall be conducted as a University agency responsible for the administration of contract research in engineering, the physical sciences, architecture, forestry, and such other fields as may appropriately be included, and of such other research within these fields as may be financially supported by funds at the disposal of the Institute. The terms and conditions of employment shall be subject to approval of the respective departments and in accord with the general policies approved by the Engineering Research Council and the Board of Regents. Employment in the Institute shall be open to graduate and under-graduate students under conditions satisfactory to the Graduate School, the Department of instruction, and the Institute, respectively, provided that such employment shall not interfere with academic tasks."

Whether it is wise for a university to foster or shun associated research organizations is a question widely debated by university administrators. The gains to a university which establishes closely associated research organizations can be substantial. Such organizations are potentially a way to bring investigators together in a stimulating environment. They can be a means of giving force and coherence to research in a selected broad field. This way of segmenting work is in theory as defensible a way of approaching the unknown as is the division of effort into the standard scientific disciplines. On a very practical plane, Alan Gregg stated a fact of life which has accounted for the establishment of many research institutes not only in medicine, but in other fields: "Separate status provides a focal point not only for the loyal energies of its members but also for the interest of its actual and potential supporters. Human loyalty seeks visible, tangible objects of manageable proportions." [5]

Associated research organizations can also generate difficulties. Simple occupancy of university buildings by an associated research organization creates management and finance problems. Many of those on the staff of the associated organizations are neither fish nor fowl. They are often paid more than faculty members of comparable ability, which makes faculty members unhappy. They do not have faculty status and perquisites, which makes them unhappy. Often the work of the associated organizations is financed by a great number of small contracts of short duration, which makes everybody unhappy.

The relation of the staff of an associated research organization to the teaching function of a university can become difficult. For example, some observers of medical schools have deplored the growth of institutes:

There is a definite tendency for workers in these institutes to become divorced from teaching . . . In numerous schools, students repeatedly said they wished they could be told about the work being carried on by the medical school in these institutes. This is a serious defect in a total research program of a school . . . Research is sharpened and the research worker is himself stimulated by close contacts with students and by their questions and criticisms.[6]

Without subscribing to the idea that associated research organizations constitute a threat to universities, it must be admitted that productive relations between those who work in the research organization and the university faculty are difficult.

The rapid rate of obsolescence of specific tasks also creates problems. A task-oriented organization associated with a university and financed with federal funds can find that the problem has either been solved or become irrelevant. In this circumstance, the survival of the organization itself, and concern for the welfare of people to whom the university has obligations, can lead to a search for funds to keep the organization intact. At times, the fate of the organization can be more significant in determining the substance of the work accepted by the organization than is the quality of the research or the contribution of the organization to the goals of the university.

M. A. Tuve, an experienced observer, has noted how this process can operate:

That there is danger of a university administration being attracted by Armed Service funds without regard to the appropriateness of an activity for university sponsorship, or to the desires and interests of the faculty members and graduate students, is illustrated by a current situation. One of our large universities, with an off-campus activity in a large facility which is being terminated, through its deans and vice-president deliberately sought a new defense project to keep the facility and its technical workers busy. After some months a new projected area of technical study having to do directly with warfare was suggested by one of the services, on a fiscal basis rapidly expanding into millions of dollars during the next several years. The university vice-president promptly accepted the contract and then notified the physics, chemistry and mathematics departments that it was their task to envolve an approach to these war problems. The assignment was accepted with great reluctance by the individuals concerned, but now the university has the expanding contract.[7]

Another aspect of this problem is illustrated by the plight of a research institute reported to me at a large university:

The Institute had plenty of Federal contracts last year, but by accident the contracts involved very little field work. But the Institute must maintain a field staff, and it took a contract for service research which it would not ordinarily have accepted. It was good sound work, but it had no particular interest to the Institute. It was undertaken simply as a stopgap measure.

Difficulties of this kind are not universal, but neither are they rare. The waste involved is greater if those associated with the research enterprise have no teaching affiliation, for in the absence of teaching responsibilities they will be idle or engaged in uncongenial work.

Even if federal funds are received for work which is perfectly congenial to the group, the person who is responsible for the group must at all costs secure contracts. The work required to obtain the contracts comes first, for the livelihood of staff members and their families depends on the success of his efforts. Those who direct such organizations are often highly capable investigators, and the time spent in seeking contracts is a real cost of no mean proportions.

Many of the problems generated for universities by the existence of associated laboratories are, in my judgment, not created by inherent incompatibility.

Alan Gregg has pointed out that the two can be articulated:

Now the advantages of having a declared and recognized separate status for an institute in a university depend in large measure on the way in which it articulates with other members of the body corporate. I like my arms to have separate parts articulating with each other by means of strong, supple and painless joints, though of course complete rigidity from shoulder to finger tips might appeal to the administrative principle of uniformity, simplicity of control and predictability of behavior.[8]

As is the case with many other aspects of the effect of federal funds on universities, an indispensable step to satisfactory resolution of problems is the establishment of clear policies at appropriate levels in the university, and firm, consistent administration of the policies. The National Science Foundation has suggested that universities take a position on the following specific questions in deciding whether an associated research organization should be established or retained by a university:

(a) Is the research to be carried on of the type that the university would not ordinarily wish to undertake?

(b) Is the required undertaking so large or costly as to seriously unbalance the academic and fiscal program of the university in maintaining it after the Government's interest has ceased?

(c) Does the undertaking require inter-university access and use?

(d) Is the research to be carried on or the equipment for it such as to create physical hazards to campus buildings and personnel?

(e) Are controlled environmental conditions required, thereby dictating a dispersed location? [9]

To which should be added the questions:

What will be the status and remuneration of the staff of the organization and what will be their teaching capacity and duties?

To what extent and in what way will the existence of the organization affect the teaching of graduate students?

Research centers

A small number of very large research organizations called "research centers," which are rather loosely associated with universities, warrant special attention. Some of the largest of the centers, of which there are about twenty operated by large universities, are these: the Jet Propulsion Laboratory at the California Institute of Technology (Army); the Applied Physics Laboratory at the Johns Hopkins University (Navy); Project Lincoln at the Massachusetts Institute of Technology (Air Force); the Los Alamos Scientific Laboratory and the Radiation Laboratories at the University of California (Atomic Energy Commission); the Argonne National Laboratory at Chicago University (AEC); and the Ames Laboratories at Iowa State College (AEC).

183

Even if the concept of a center is interpreted broadly, there are only about 20 centers currently. Each of the centers operated by universities is unique in certain respects. This variation in the structure and functions of the centers can be epitomized by a brief description of three operated by the University of California.

The Radiation Laboratory is located on the hill next to the Berkeley campus. Established as an academic organization, it was financed first with private funds, later with government funds. Most of the work is classified, but a great deal of the research is on basic problems in nuclear physics. From 200 to 250 graduate students work in the Radiation Laboratory at any one time. All are referred by the Berkeley Department of Physics. About 70 Ph.D. theses in the Department of Physics each year are based on work done at the laboratory. Professional salaries at the laboratory are comparable to those at the university although exceptions are made to secure and keep good people.

The gigantic particle accelerator called the bevatron and other large equipment of the Radiation Laboratory set it apart from the other centers operated by the University. The Radiation Laboratory is in effect another campus of the University of California, a sort of subuniversity for the study of atomic physics. The Director of the Laboratory has the unofficial status of chancellor. Livermore is a smaller research organization, located about 40 miles from Berkeley, devoted primarily to theoretical problems having largely to do with atomic fusion. Much of the work is classified. The Livermore Laboratory does not have extremely large equipment, and the staff is not so closely associated with the department of physics as the staff of the Radiation Laboratory.

Los Alamos, famed as the laboratory where the first atomic bomb was developed, though managed by the University of California, is hundreds of miles from Berkeley. Sheer distance makes the operation of the laboratory remote from the other affairs of this university. Graduate students work at Los Alamos, but it is not an academic center of the stature of the Radiation Laboratory. Los Alamos has experienced vicissitudes since the war, including an exodus of staff followed by shifts in the budget level and changes in leadership. Unlike the Radiation Laboratory, Los Alamos was created to work on the atomic bomb and has always been completely financed by the government.

Despite diversity, the centers share important characteristics with other associated research organizations: wide power to set personnel policy, complete dependence on federal funds, federal ownership of physical facilities, establishment of the mission of the organization in cooperation with a federal agency, and major — if not exclusive — concentration upon research as contrasted with the teaching task.

The characteristic which distinguishes the centers from other university-associated laboratories is size. The operating budgets of these organizations range up to $50 million a year (Table 13).

Table 13. Cost of major research centers operated by universities for the Atomic Energy Commission, 1957 (millions of dollars)

Research Center	Number of contractor employees	Investment in completed plant 6/30/57	Operating costs FY 1957
Total	12,250	329	148
Los Alamos Scientific Laboratory	3,300	123	55
Argonne National Laboratory	2,900	88	29
Brookhaven National Laboratory	1,750	59	17
Radiation Laboratory, Berkeley & Livermore	4,300	59	47

Source: United States Atomic Energy Commission, *1957 Financial Report* (Washington: Government Printing Office, 1957), p. 20.

The centers employ as many as 4,000 people each and well over 15,000 in total. The sheer size of the research center operations is indicated by the $200 million spent by the federal government for the operation of research centers in the fiscal year 1959. As much federal money is spent for the operation of a few research centers as for all support of individual faculty members, and all other research organizations associated with universities.

The research centers were a brilliant innovation and most of them have done a superb job. The comments of President Du Bridge of the California Institute of Technology are typical:

To my mind the most successful laboratories for turning out new ideas, new equipment, and new techniques for the military services are those operated under management contracts' . . . government-owned laboratories under private management. These 'research centers' as they are often called have in many cases been brilliantly productive. They have the ad-

185

vantages of private, civilian, noncivil-service management. And yet, being government-owned, they can be kept in close touch with the practical problems of the sponsoring agency.[10]

Large and complex as the research centers are, they do not create major day-to-day operating and policy problems for universities. The centers are rarely financial drains on the universities. The staff members typically do little teaching. All capital and operating costs are borne by the federal government. Physical and administrative separation of the centers and the university tends to create staff acceptance of the legal fact that the university has no responsibilities as an employer. Dr. Frederick Lindvall of the California Institute of Technology made the following remarks, still applicable to a number of university managed research centers:

> We have a Jet Propulsion Laboratory, which is an inheritance from the war days. It was built entirely with public money and is completely owned by the government. Tech still has operating contracts for conducting the research there. Three hundred and fifty persons, roughly, are on the Jet Propulsion Laboratory pay roll. Exactly three of our permanent faculty have part-time connection with the Jet Propulsion Laboratory . . . The show is completely off campus . . . The operation could convert tomorrow to a civil service status, and I, for one, would welcome it. I think the nuisance of taking care of it is more than the good that accrues . . . There is a scramble over the overhead for running it, but we won't worry about accounting philosophy.[11]

Of course, the relation between some research centers and universities is closer and more productive than in the case of the California Institute of Technology and the Jet Propulsion Laboratory. The work at some research centers is congenial to the university atmosphere and contributes to the academic life of the university. The University of California, for example, would lose both teaching and research strength if it were divorced from the Radiation Laboratory.

In view of the prevailing remoteness of centers from universities, do they have any effects at all on universities? They most decidedly do, particularly through their general influence as contrasted with the effects of one center on the university to which it is attached. Research centers compete with universities for scarce manpower. A well-managed center is a better place to do research than many universities. Many investigators in research centers totally financed by the government are in fact much freer than their university friends whose work is financed in part by federal contracts for relatively small amounts, for relatively short periods. Moreover, the research centers usually pay higher salaries than universities. And for those — and there are many — whose research is stimulated more by continuing contact with mature minds than with maturing minds, the centers offer an opportunity to work full time at research.

The competition of centers for manpower, added to the competition from industrial, government, and foundation laboratories, creates problems for universities, whether or not the centers are associated with universities. As was noted in Chapter 8, the problem exists not because salaries paid to scientists in research center or in industry are excessive or "out of balance," but because university salary scales are too low. Since universities cannot now compete on the basis of salary, they must compete, as they always have, largely on the basis of noneconomic factors. Among these, the most significant is the maintenance of freedom and of the intangibles that contribute to freedom.

Research centers are potentially a means of siphoning off from universities, if universities wish to seize the opportunity, research which involves a diminution of the freedom of faculty members. Several years ago, Alan Waterman noted the relation of research organizations attached to universities to freedom:

They can accept support for applied research or development with less fear of upsetting the balance between education, basic research, and applied research. They can more readily go in for group research and more extensive programs. To some extent they can protect the university from sudden fluctuations in financial support. They can more readily accommodate confidential work, either from industry or government.[12]

In all probability, large-scale federally financed research will continue to grow. Search for the attainment of vital national goals through research, most notably national defense, will be vigorously prosecuted through research centers.

Much of this research must be performed by large research organizations. The research centers should be considered not as competitors of the university but rather as catch basins into which can drain the large-scale research and development which is indispensable to national defense, but not congenial to universities. Research of this character will tend progressively to inundate universities if other sites for the effective prosecution of the urgently needed work are not available.

Summary

The wide variety of new research organizations associated with universities, ranging in a continuum from existing departments which have made minor readjustments, to gigantic research centers remotely attached to universities, reflect the need to adapt administrative forms to the extreme pressures exerted by the federal funds. The most significant questions do not relate to these forms themselves. The administrative structures can be the instrument for the reconciliation of the imperative federal need for large-scale research and the imperative need to sustain universities as the site for the free inquiry of individuals. On the other hand, the administrative structures can operate as a disruptive force and impede the attainment of a productive reconciliation between the goals of the federal agencies and those of universities.

11

University Participation in Federal Decisions

Relations between universities and the federal government have existed since Washington proposed the establishment of a national university in 1796.[1] The establishment of the land grant colleges, and of federal grants to colleges of the agriculture and mechanic arts under the second Morrill Act of 1890, extended and complicated the relations. The first general mechanism through which universities could deal with the federal government was the National Academy of Sciences, founded in 1863. Between World War I and World War II, the National Research Council, an adjunct of the Academy, was the primary channel of communication between universities and the government. Communication was largely in one direction — advice from university scientists on the operation and programs of federal laboratories. The advice was in fact neither frequent nor significant, for the National Research Council was much more strongly oriented to the private foundations than to the federal government. This was natural because the private foundations were during that period a stronger force in science than was the federal government.

World War II shifted the problem quickly and drastically. The core of the task was to mobilize the nation's scientists for war work. The National Research Council was not constituted to perform that task adequately. The job was done by a newly created

Office of Scientific Research and Development. After World War II, the OSRD programs were taken over by the regular agencies of government, and new programs for the support of research were inaugurated by various federal agencies, and grew to an unprecedented size. This state of affairs has no resemblance to that existing before the war. In the postwar period, universities have been interested in the federal government not as the operator of some small research enterprises which need advice occasionally, but as a major source of funds, a competitor for scientific manpower, and a powerful influence upon university affairs.

Faculty members and universities must now deal directly with the individual federal agencies because too much is at stake to use an intermediary. They have an interest in seeing that the government machinery for handling research funds is well designed and well operated. They must, as a matter of self-protection, undertake to affect such matters as the terms and conditions under which funds are made available to universities. If universities do not participate in both the formulation and the execution of the research policies of federal agencies, many decisions in which they have a vital interest will be made for them by others. This interest leads universities to press for influence in various ways and among the most important of these is representation on federal scientific advisory bodies.

Federal agencies have a compelling need to draw representatives of universities, and faculty members as scientists, into the scientific activities of the federal government in different capacities and at different levels. The agencies typically want to select advisers themselves. They want to present problems to advisers directly and not through an intermediary. They need the support of advisers in important dealings within the executive branch, with Congress, and with the public.

These institutional needs explain why direct relations between faculty members and federal officials have proliferated in the postwar period. One consequence of this direct dealing has been a rise in the number and significance of scientific groups which advise federal agencies directly, and a decline in the relative importance of the National Research Council as the intermediary between federal agencies and universities.

Structure

Every federal agency which finances research in universities utilizes the advice of groups of scientists drawn largely from universities. The characteristics of these groups — such as the authority under which they are established, the reliance placed on their advice and the level in the administrative hierarchy at which their advice is rendered — vary widely.[2] But underlying the diversity of the system, which is briefly sketched below, are some common virtues and some general problems which it creates for the advisers and for the advised.

The administrative level at which advice is given ranges from single laboratories to Cabinet members. In general, the broader the problems with which the advisory group deals, the nearer to the top of the administrative pyramid is advice given. For example, a Naval Research Advisory Committee advises the Secretary of the Navy, the Chief of Naval Operations, and the Chief of Naval Research on questions of research policy pertaining to the Navy Department. At the same time, the Office of Naval Research has not only a top advisory committee but also a number of technical committees and panels which consider individual research projects. Another example is the Public Health Service, which has National Advisory Councils whose membership, chairmen, and functions are established by law. These groups deal with general policy problems of research support as well as with individual research grants. The Surgeon General is the *ex-officio* chairman of all these groups. In addition, the Public Health Service has established by administrative action some 25 technical panels, called "study sections." These groups, composed of scientists and with chairmen named by the Public Health Service, concern themselves primarily with technical matters. Their judgments are, with rare exceptions, accepted by the statutory advisory councils and by the administrative staff.

How formally the advisory groups are established and how much reliance is placed upon their advice vary widely. Some groups — for example, the Naval Research Advisory Committee, the Divisional Committees of the National Science Foundation, the Agricultural Research Policy Committee of the Department of Agriculture, and the National Advisory Councils of the Public Health Service — are created by statute. Other groups are formally created by administrative action. Finally, some research organizations rely upon panels of advisers who do not necessarily meet as groups. For example, the Office of Scientific Research of the Air Research and Development Command sends contract proposals to individuals in universities. Whether the advice of such "referees" is sought or not depends on the judgment of the full-time civilian scientific staff of the Office.

Some federal agencies depend much more than others on the opinions offered by advisory groups. At one extreme is the unique statutory provision requiring that the National Advisory Councils of the Public Health Service recommend payment of each research grant before the responsible administrative officer, the Surgeon General of the Public Health Service, may approve payment. At the other extreme are advisory groups which render advice upon the general emphasis of research grant and contract programs.

The greater the reliance placed upon advisory groups, the less significant is the judgment of full-time federal employees. The Divisions of Biology and Medicine and of Physical Sciences of the Atomic Energy Commission rely heavily upon staff judgments with respect to research contracts, while the administratively created groups advisory to these Divisions confine their advice almost entirely to general trends in the total program. The staff of the National Science Foundation exercises wide powers of decision, while the statutory Divisional Committees ratify and to some extent modify staff decisions. On the other hand, the administratively created technical study sections of the National Institutes of Health, composed primarily of scientists from universities, have much more to say about the disposition of individual requests for research grants than does the staff of the Institutes.

Composition and cost

The composition of scientific advisory groups depends upon the kind of advice which the groups are asked to provide. If the decisions are purely technical, active scientists are asked to serve.

If research grants go entirely to academic institutions, few industrial advisers will be found on the advisory groups; but if a federal program involves industrial research contracts, the industrial point of view will typically be presented by advisers from industrial research laboratories. When the groups concern themselves with general questions of science policy, informed nonscientists are often members of the advisory groups.

While the precise number of advisers is not known, they probably number well above a thousand (Table 14). When one recalls

Table 14. Composition of advisory groups, by kind of institution

Affiliation of Adviser	Number	Percent
Total	651	100
Academic institutions	412	63
Industry	83	13
Hospitals	60	9
Research facilities	27	4
Foundations	10	2
Other	59	9

Source: National Science Foundation, unpublished report.

that scientists judged by their peers to be most capable serve on these groups, the significance of using the advisory groups effectively becomes clear. Heavy reliance is placed upon advisers from universities.

The most significant cost of the advisory system is the time which highly qualified people spend away from their research, university teaching, or university administration. The system is costly to operate in terms of dollars expended too. Consultants usually are reimbursed for their travel expenses and in addition they receive from $25 to $50 a day for their services, at a total cost of several million dollars a year.

Is there any way in which the substantial cost of the system — in terms of money or time — might be reduced?

Since the number of decisions required of technical groups is in almost direct proportion to the average size of grants or contracts, an increase in the size of grants or contracts seems to be one way to reduce substantially the volume of advisory work. Another possible economy measure is to adopt the unwise course of sharply reducing the quality of the review. Consolidating the consideration of requests for funds within given fields of science might be a third way of reducing the cost of the system. For example, technical advisory groups to the Armed Forces Epidemiological Board, the National Science Foundation, and the National Institutes of Health consider requests for support in the field of microbiology. One group might consider the whole batch. Such a procedure would, however, substitute the superficial advantage of administrative simplicity for the fundamental advantage of sustaining diversity of judgment.

In short, any substantial streamlining of the advisory system must depend on the resolution of the fundamental question whether federal support of research in universities will take the form of small sums for specific work, or large sums for more generally defined research.

Functions of the system

The scientific advisory groups counsel on matters ranging from purely technical to broad scientific strategy. At a technical level, knowledge of the substance of science in highly specialized fields, and knowledge of the facilities and people available for work in these fields, are prerequisites to sound decisions. The federal agencies cannot employ the necessary talent full time. Part-time advice is clearly called for, and university staffs are necessarily drawn upon heavily.

On technical matters, federal scientific advisers are extremely influential. One perceptive participant in the advisory system, C. P. Richter of the Johns Hopkins University, assessed the system from the point of view of scientists in these terms:

We are participants in a great revolutionary movement. For the first time we, as scientists, are beginning to hold the responsibility for our future in our own hands. We are asked to pass not only on the scientific merit of the work of our colleagues, but on its anticipated merits for financial support . . . Now support comes in large part from the various government agencies — a few large public organizations — and funds for research are channelled most exclusively through committees of scientists . . . This gives us much power and responsibility — more than we may realize.[3]

This comment relates to programs under which the initiative

lies with the investigator and the area of research is not linked to the performance of a departmental operating mission. In this situation, advisory groups often screen individual research project proposals, comment upon the proposed budget, rank the proposals in priority order, and in fact exercise the predominant voice in selection of recipients of federal research funds. When a department has a specific problem which it wants investigated and seeks out someone to study the problem, technical advice from part-time groups is less important but still influential. Scientific advisers exercise more influence over federal programs for the purchase or support of research in nonfederal laboratories than they do over the programs of federal laboratories.

Some advisory groups deal with general research policies of various kinds. For example, a number of advisory groups review broad fields of research in an effort to determine whether the general emphasis of the federal assistance is best calculated to advance the field in question. These groups often advise not only upon the substance of research but also upon the terms and conditions under which research funds should be made available.

Advice of this general kind exerts a substantial influence upon the development and emphasis of work within fields of science. Indeed, federal funds have served as a means of substantially reorganizing the process through which the collective judgment of experts influences, without controlling, the content and general direction of scientific effort.

Advisers have had less influence on the terms and conditions of grants and contracts than on the substance of the research financed.

Universities have been drawn into participation in the process of decision-making on scientific matters not only through the service of faculty members on standing scientific advisory groups, but also through their service on so-called "study groups." (The strategic questions dealt with by the study groups are stated or clearly implied in testimony given "In the Matter of J. Robert Oppenheimer" before the Personnel Security Board.[4] Although technical details do not appear in the transcript of the proceedings, most of the essential policy questions raised for strategic military planning by postwar technical advances in nuclear science

195

and technology are clearly set forth. The detailed testimony of those who participated in the most critical military-scientific-political discussions provides a picture of the process of decision-making in this sphere.)

These groups provide advice on broad strategic problems which are heavily intertwined with scientific and technical considerations. They have generally been set up informally on an *ad hoc* basis by the Atomic Energy Commission and parts of the Department of Defense. Among the groups have been the Lexington Study to investigate nuclear-powered flight, Project East River to advise on problems of civil defense, the Lincoln Summer Study Project dealing with continental air defense, the Hartwell Project to study the problem of maintaining transport over the seas during wartime, and Project Vista to develop systems of tactics and strategy for a number of nuclear weapons.

These studies have involved university faculty members, and universities themselves, in decisions of very great consequence to the nation. As Don Price has noted, "The United States is the only nation that has ever been willing to support and create private institutions to make studies on problems combining scientific and military considerations — problems of a sort that would elsewhere be considered the very heart of general staff planning. The private institutions that are now largely supported by military funds are the most important sources of independent, sceptical, and uninhibited criticism of military thinking. And independent criticism is the basis of freedom in any political mechanism." [5]

Despite the weight usually given to the advice of study groups, the *de facto* authority of scientific advisory groups to make decisions on scientific matters for full-time administrators typically declines as the problems on which advice is given move progressively from purely scientific matters to those of broad policy. This decline in influence is fundamentally desirable because the broader the problem of government to be solved, the broader the kinds of considerations that should be taken into account. A national policy for science develops much like domestic tax policy, farm policy, resource development policy, or foreign policy. The streams of thought, the kinds of pressures, the balances of forces that properly and necessarily enter into the determination of all national policies are so numerous that the effect of any single influence is merged with others in the process of reaching a democratic solution.

In part by design and in part by accident, most federal scientific advisory groups dealing either with technical or policy problems have functions other than providing judgments on questions of scientific tactics and strategy. Advisory groups can be, and many are, sounding boards on which to test proposed policies and means of communicating with interest groups. Most important, the groups are a means of rallying support — including congressional support — for the programs of the various agencies.

The fact that decisions conventionally thought of as governmental are made by advisory groups to federal agencies has attracted attention in Congress. In 1957, for example, Representative Dawson of Illinois introduced a bill (H.R. 7390) to require certain minimum reporting requirements by these groups. The report accompanying the bill (Report No. 576, 85th Congress, 1st Session) noted that, "The committee is in full accord with the basic theory behind the advisory committee system, but it also realizes that . . . it is possible and entirely probable that some of them are established not for the primary purpose of giving advice."

The propensity of congressional committees to heed the advice of technical experts on matters of general policy, as well as on matters in which the experts are professionally qualified, makes the large group of scientific advisers a potent source of support for appropriations, for substantive legislation desired by federal agencies and for broad policies desired by both the advisers and the advised. For example, outside advisory groups are a protection against the possibility that Congress will direct the distribution of research funds by formula, a possibility viewed with aversion by the executive agencies and by most universities. Indeed a system for selecting, on the basis of judgments and without congressional review, a small number of individuals and institutions as recipients of large sums could hardly survive without an outside advisory group to act as an adjunct to congressional committees in reviewing the way the executive agencies use the broad research authority conferred on them by Congress.

These unofficial and often unarticulated functions of scientific advisory groups are fully as important as their stated functions. The emergence of this new administrative instrument has significant implications for universities. It brings faculty members and administrative officers squarely into the political process by which the most significant questions relating to the research activities of the federal government are, and should be, settled.

Advisers and control of research

The scientific advisory system is one under which part-time advisers who cannot be held responsible in a legal sense are given authority to make decisions for agencies of the federal government, including the distribution of funds for research. Such a system inevitably generates problems for the advisers and the advised.

The use of advisory groups creates a potential danger of undue control of investigators. As federal funds have become the major source of research conducted in universities, the process of deciding who will receive funds has necessarily become impersonal. In the absence of personal knowledge of investigators, advisory groups have had to rely heavily on written applications, proposals, or bids. Richter has remarked of this process that:

> In making an application for a grant before World War II, a few lines or at most a paragraph or two sufficed for the experimental design; now it may extend 6–8 single-spaced typewritten pages . . . Although done in good faith, this questioning of details by committee members often serves no other purpose than the inflation of our egos, especially when the applicant is a man of some importance. Under these circumstances, passing the buck has come to be practiced very widely . . . This is a wasteful, time-consuming, discouraging practice.[6]

Unless the technical groups themselves, the advisers with review functions, and the federal administrators are constantly aware of the way in which insistence upon extreme detail and reluctance to make decisions can gradually permeate the advisory process, decisions exerting onerous and unnecessary control over research will be made. While the system is not free of the defects pointed out by Dr. Richter, the effectiveness of the system as a whole is not seriously impaired by inappropriate demands for the minutiae of proposed research.

Of course, the absence of overt control over the work of investigators does not mean that control could not be exercised by more subtle means. For one thing, favoritism of various kinds might influence the distribution of funds and hence in a sense control individuals even though they are left completely free after decisions are made. Favoritism to themselves, to their institutions or their friends, to geographic areas, or to schools of thought is possible in a system which gives advisers an important voice in the distribution of federal research funds.

One objection made to the present system is that it enables the advisers to favor themselves by stealing research ideas presented to them for judgment. However, in conversations with some scientists who have received and others who have been denied federal support, I have encountered no one who felt that advisers abused the power of their positions in this manner. Since the academic grapevine is a powerful means of communication, the odds are that any adviser who lifted an idea from a colleague could not prevent his action from becoming known. Moreover, applications for federal support are phrased so generally that whatever really new ideas the applicant may have rarely appear.

Complaints of favoritism based upon scientific, institutional, or geographic bias have been rare. The most conspicuous example is an article in *Science* by C. A. Mills, of the University of Cincinnati.[7] He contended that the heavy concentration of research support on the eastern seaboard reflected bias on the part of federal agencies and their advisers, but this cannot be demonstrated. The geographical distribution of advisers follows almost exactly the geographical distribution of talent as indicated by the number of people listed in *American Men of Science*.

It should be noted that there are no interlocking directorates among advisory groups. Although there are some Pooh-Bahs in the advisory business, few advisers hold more than one membership at a time. A recent unpublished study by the National Science Foundation of 100 scientific advisory bodies with a total membership of 767 persons, found only 21 persons — 3 percent — with membership in more than one group. The generally accepted policies of rotation of membership and selection of advisers by administrators rather than by the groups themselves further protect against the self-perpetuation of a single group with undue influence.

A species of favoritism for the safe, known, and proven as against the new, novel, and unusual proposal may be built into the scientific advisory system. W. H. Whyte has pointed out in *The Organization Man* why this is sometimes the case with scientific advisory groups:

> A committee member might be inclined to support an idea, but he is also not inclined to put up the fight for it that will be needed. He is constrained by good will. He feels an obligation to his fellow committeemen, who are, after all, only trying to do a good job, like himself. So he compromises, not from mere timidity, but from a real desire to show respect for the opinion of others.[8]

But even if too high a proportion of decisions are reached as the result of unwise compromises, which I doubt, the problem of refusing to give an unorthodox idea a chance would not be resolved by remanding the effective power of decision to full-time federal employees. Pressures toward respect for orthodoxy and away from taking a chance are much greater on full-time federal officials, alone or in groups, than on part-time advisers. When the alternative is decision by full-time federal officials a disinclination to take a scientific flyer in the face of conservative advice cannot be considered a valid objection to the use of scientific advisory groups.

In conclusion, several powerful forces sharply restrict the possibility of favoritism. Federal officials are typically sensitive to the potential dangers, and all of them are ultimately accountable to a Congress which keeps a close eye on geographical representation. The loyalty of advisers toward their professional fields as contrasted with their universities also helps avoid institutional favoritism. Deliberate attention to diversity of institutional, geographical, and scientific points of view in the selection of advisers militates against the entrenchment of specialized interests. The number of advisory groups, together with their overlapping functions, ensure effective representation of various viewpoints. Extensive use of part-time scientific advisory groups places the process of making decisions in a goldfish bowl. Finally, review of technical decisions by advisory or administrative groups at a higher level is a protection against favoritism.

Transfer of initiative and authority

Before World War II, the research money available to universities was distributed either by mechanisms within the university itself, or by the full-time staffs of large foundations. Now that 70 percent of all university research funds are provided by federal agencies which rely heavily upon university advisory groups, the system is fundamentally different. By establishing scientific advisory groups, federal agencies have thoroughly restructured the machinery for distributing research funds. The primary characteristic of the new system is the organization of the total scientific community by discipline or by field to make decisions formerly made within individual universities, or by the staffs of foundations. This is particularly true when research is supported, for when research is purchased many of the specifications for research are properly laid down by the buyer.

There is much to be said for this new way of deciding who will be supported. For one thing, the system decentralizes and democratizes the process of deciding what research is worth doing, who should do it, and what resources should be made available to individuals. As a result, the image of a powerful centralized bureaucracy in control of the nation's research is highly unrealistic. Never have the scientists of the nation had so much authority over the funds which they receive.

The system provides not only wide participation, but a means of applying high competence to technical decisions. There is widespread agreement that the intelligence applied through the advisory system to decisions on specific research proposals and to the scientific capacity of individuals is superior to the intelligence brought to bear when decisions are made within individual faculties or by foundation staffs.

Transfer of an important share of decisions on research to scientists organized outside of universities has some important implications for universities. For one thing, universities may have assented too easily in the transfer of authority. Their reasons for assenting are understandable. The competence available in groups selected on a nationwide basis is generally of a higher order than that found on a single campus. Moreover, decisions made within a single university on the distribution of research money are difficult, largely because they tend to involve personalities to a greater degree than do decisions made by a national group. But when control of all the parts is relinquished, control of the whole is relinquished. The extensive readjustment of university administrative structure in response to research needs, described in the preceding chapter, is in large part an effort to recapture their former share of the power of decision on research matters.

Responsiveness and responsibility

While the scientific advisory system is a powerful, flexible machine for research administration, it is not easy to manage in a manner reconciling the legitimate demands of science and government. Full-time federal officials are responsible to Congress for the administration of laws. They cannot delegate responsibility for matters which the Congress properly holds them accountable to advisers over whom Congress has no control. The officials who are advised must ensure that the advice is offered on matters and in a way which does not involve improper delegation of authority. On the other hand, the advisers waste their time if their counsel is not generally accepted. Attainment of the proper relation between advisers and the advised is perhaps the most important and difficult problem created by the use of scientific advisory groups.

It is more difficult to keep advisory groups responsive to the needs of the advised when research is purchased than when it is supported. Purchased research is designed to meet the operating requirements of federal agencies. These needs set the general shape of the research to be purchased, and technical advisers must work within rather fixed limits if their advice is to be useful. For example, advice to the Department of the Air Force on a research contract relating to development of a weapon must be given not only in the light of judgments as to the competence of potential contractors and the merits of the weapon in the abstract, but also within limits set by the mission of the Air Force and by the total system of which the weapon is a part. Advice is useful only to the extent that advisers understand the full range of factors surrounding the problem on which they are advising.

On the other hand, when technical advice is given on supported research, the most significant factors affecting decisions are within the scientific sphere, and the operating needs of the agencies have much less effect upon individual decisions. Within wide limits set by the general research charters of the agencies, heavy reliance can be placed upon the ability of the scientist himself apart from what he proposes to investigate.

Since the area of effective decision left to scientific advisers in this circumstance is wide, no improper abdication of executive responsibility is involved. While formal authority to authorize the expenditure of federal funds must remain with federal officials who are accountable to Congress, the primary responsibility of the federal agencies is not in this circumstance to arrive at judgments on the worth of proposed research and the ability of investigators. The primary responsibility of the federal agency is to see that the machinery operates so that competent men may make impartial decisions on the substance of science and to the capacity of individuals.

Management of a scientific advisory system so that it serves a proper role well is not an easy task, whether the advisers work with a program under which research is purchased or supported. The full-time officials must, for example, ensure that the system operates without favoritism and that technical advisers do not take on inappropriate general policy functions. They must also ensure that the participation of advisers in general executive processes, such as the formulation of the executive budget, involves no improper devolving of responsibility, improper disclosure, or political pressure.

At the same time, administrators must undertake to set the deliberations of advisory groups at a level which will permit them to contribute to the construction of policies. This is sometimes difficult because of the way the groups themselves act and the way in which federal research policy in fact develops.

Advisory groups can acquire institutional views of their own. When a group of part-time advisers become accustomed to a given set of policies, they can become attached to the *status quo* and lose the ability to adjust easily and flexibly to changed conditions. The advisory bureaucracy created by the responsible bureaucracy is at times less responsive to evolving scientific needs than those who have sought advice. The motive force for adaptability may, therefore, have to come from the federal administrative staff rather than from advisory groups.

The possibility of inappropriate authority over policy by advisory groups is also reduced by the way in which research policy is formed. Often, "policy" is not arrived at by the adoption of carefully considered lines of action formulated before the fact and near the top of the administrative hierarchy. A federal research policy is often the recognition of a *fait accompli* created by a long series of apparently trivial decisions made near the bottom of the administrative hierarchy. In this process of policy formulation the scientific adviser is at times and in a certain sense a captive. For example, an adviser from a university who serves on a policy advisory group may feel that the federal agency is asking universities to undertake work of a routine nature which is, in his opinion, inappropriate. But if the full-time staff of the agency strongly urges that such work be contracted out to a university, the adviser is not likely to interpose strong objections. He may believe that he should hold his fire for more significant issues. But these significant issues are most often not presented in a clear-cut manner. Hence, it is often difficult for consultants to "advise on policy" with a high degree of realism and independence, even when they are asked in good faith to do so.

While scientific advisory groups rarely assume the authority to make general policies appropriately formulated by responsible officials, the advisers do at times approach or even cross the boundary of propriety in acting as advocates for the advised. Not uncommonly, people who serve in advisory positions do so because they have not only technical competence, broad understanding, and perception, but also influence outside and inside their immediate professional circles. The qualities that make them influential are the same qualities that make them valuable as advisers. Advisers are generally sympathetic with the objectives of the program. In this situation, it is natural that a substantial number of advisers actively support the programs on which they render advice and become the allies of the administrators. Here complications arise because most federal research organizations are bureaus or parts of bureaus with special institutional interests that are not always best advanced by the policies and actions of the department of which they are a part. This situation can be particularly difficult when the advisers lobby or testify in any private or public capacity in Congress for federal research programs. Advisers may, in becoming allies of the bureau chiefs and the congressional committees interested in their activities, abet the opposition of bureau chiefs and of chairmen of congressional committees to the continuing effort to sustain an executive structure responsible to the President and a Congress responsible to the needs of the nation.

The gaps

The system of scientific advisory bodies is, by and large, admirably suited to help the parts of the executive branch that are concerned with research do what they want to do in the way they want to do it.

On the other hand, the system, which has grown in a productively haphazard way, is not designed to contribute to the formulation of a coherent set of general science policies for the federal government as a whole.

Similarly, the scientific advisory system was not devised to serve universities, and universities benefit from the operation of the system only incidentally, and only because they would probably be worse off if the advisory structure did not exist. What universities need, through one device or another, is a means of controlling to a greater degree the total volume of funds coming to the institution and the terms and conditions under which research funds are made available. So long as a multitude of small grants and contracts of a relatively short-term character are made to one university through a number of federal agencies, it is in practice difficult for representatives of that university to use the system so that the needs and the potential contribution of a university as a whole can be taken into account.

12

Conclusion

Universities need support for science from government, and government needs knowledge obtainable only by university research. As a result, the two have been placed in a state of unprecedented mutual dependence. The nature and degree of this relation, and the effects of federal research funds on universities and on the federal government, are what this book is about. The preceding chapters have dealt with an aspect of one of the most important questions of our time — the relations between science and society.

Science and society

Federal funds are a force outside science which organizes and directs science. They are one important way through which society exerts pressure on science. Whether these forces can be exerted without reducing the freedom and productivity of science and of the universities is an intricate question which lies at the root of most of the questions discussed earlier.

Some philosophers of science have maintained that any external forces tending to direct the substance of science must be pernicious. Michael Polanyi, a philosophical liberal to whom the freedom of the individual scientist is an article of faith, takes this position:

No committee of scientists, however distinguished, could forecast the further progress of science except for the routine extension of the existing system . . . The pursuit of science can be organized, therefore, in no other manner than by granting complete independence to all mature scien-

206

tists . . . The function of public authorities is not to plan research, but only to provide opportunities for its pursuit . . . To do less is to neglect the progress of science; to do more is to cultivate mediocrity and waste public money.[1]

If he is right, our federal government is undertaking to influence the direction of science in a way which inherently cultivates mediocrity and wastes public money.

Polanyi's view is not universal. The most extreme dissent is expressed by those who see science as the servant of a materialistically determined state. Bernal and Hogben have stated this view in the context of a consistent philosophy. Bernal, for example, wrote that:

The relevance of Marxism to science is that it removes it from its position of complete detachment and shows it as a part, but a critically important part, of economic and social development . . . Science should provide a continuous series of unpredictable radical changes in the techniques themselves. Whether these changes fit in or fail to fit in with human and social needs is a measure of how far science has been adjusted to its social function.[2]

Hogben has stated a variation on the same theme:

To get the fullest opportunities for doing the kind of work which is worthwhile to themselves scientific workers must participate in their responsibilities as citizens. Among other things, this includes refraining from the arrogant pretence that their own preferences are a sufficient justification for the support which they need. This pretence, put forward as the plea that science should be encouraged for its own sake, is a survival of Platonism and of the city-state tradition of slave ownership. Science thrives by its applications. To justify it as an end in itself is a policy of defeat.[3]

George Sarton has stated a middle position which seems to me esthetically and logically more satisfactory:

Great social events cast their shadows before and after upon science as well as upon other human activities; and however alive and independent science may ever be, it never develops in a political vacuum. Yet each scientific question suggests irresistably new questions connected with it by no bounds but the bounds of logic. Each new discovery exerts as it were a pressure in a new direction, and causes the growth of a new branch of science, or at least of a new twig. The whole fabric of science seems thus to be growing like a tree; in both cases the dependence upon the environment is obvious enough, yet the main cause of growth — the growth pressure, the urge to grow — is inside the tree, not outside. Thus science is as it were independent of particular people, though it may be affected at sundry times by each of them.[4]

The question that must be asked is — to pursue Sarton's analogy — whether the environment for science created by federal funds is healthy or unhealthy.

Causes and effects

Those in the physical sciences have difficulty in describing situations fully, and in establishing ultimate cause and effect relations. It should therefore be taken for granted that the effects of federal research funds on universities cannot be determined objectively and precisely.

Cultural pressures. The primary reason for uncertainty is that neither the federal government nor universities exist independent of the culture of which they are parts. The omnipresent force of the values of men affect both universities and federal agencies.

One of these forces has been our persisting predilection for the practical, in the sense of the immediately useful. This trait, as de Tocqueville pointed out in 1831, has fostered applied as contrasted with fundamental science:

In America, the purely practical part of science is admirably understood, and careful attention is paid to the theoretical portion which is immediately requisite to application. On this head, the Americans always display a clear, free, original and inventive power of mind.

Men who live in democratic communities not only seldom indulge in meditation but they naturally entertain very little esteem for it . . .

Possessing education and freedom, men living in democratic ages cannot fail to improve the industrial part of science . . . The local conditions and the institutions of democracy prepare scientists to seek the immediate and useful practical results of the sciences.[5]

This national characteristic affects universities as well as federal agencies. In some universities good applied work is valued more highly than good fundamental work. Many faculty members prefer to conduct applied research although funds are available for basic research and the government exerts no pressure on them to do applied work; they are trained for and happy with applied work. For these reasons, the emphasis of university research would not shift markedly towards the basic end of the spectrum if unlimited federal funds were available without strings.

Another force that operates upon both universities and federal agencies is a national tendency to seek bigness as an end in itself. Speaking of university scientists, Paul Klopsteg, the Associate Director of the National Science Foundation, has noted that:

> In their feeling of need for financial aid and their desire to initiate team work, they did not discriminate between the military developments on which they had worked and their own pre-war basic research. The new pattern of large operations had been extended, in their minds, to include their own work. They would be greatly handicapped unless they had a great deal of money and many assistants. In many instances, their university administrations were easily persuaded to adopt the same view.[6]

Since World War II, faith in the power of research has become a national characteristic. The federal government contributed heavily to this development, notably through the development of the atomic bomb. However, widespread acceptance of the efficacy of research, coupled with a mistrust of scientists, has deeper roots. Faith in the power of science has strongly influenced both federal agencies and universities in the postwar years. Medical schools, for example, are conducting research on a scale out of balance with their teaching and community service responsibilities. Since about half of the research is financed by federal agencies, they are often held responsible for creating this imbalance; but the federal agencies and the medical schools are the expression of a national faith in the power of research.

Since pressures for growth are exerted by general cultural pressures, the federal funds have "caused" the growth of research in universities only in a limited sense.

Forces within universities. Forces generated within universities themselves have conditioned the effects of federal research funds. For example, the tradition of service to government is strong, particularly among the tax-supported institutions. They feel an obligation to make their faculties available for government research.

Federal funds have provided the means by which universities could caricature themselves if they so desired. Some universities which have wanted to establish large applied research enterprises have been able to finance the expansion with federal funds. Conversely, those universities which have held to rigorous standards of scholarship and intellectual excellence have been able through self-discipline to avoid untoward effects of federal funds, and to use them productively.

The most significant factor affecting university research programs has not been the federal government but the standards of excellence and discrimination maintained by the intangible social pressures of the faculty. The most important effect of the federal funds has therefore been to provide momentum in directions set by cultural values and by forces within universities.

Federal authority. The executive and legislative branches of government do, however, decide some important matters affecting university research. By law Congress controls appropriations, an important power. But the executive agencies also have a great deal to say about the level of research appropriations, despite the power of Congress to appropriate. They also have wide latitude to determine the kind of research that will be supported and where it will be done. For example, they have largely independent authority to decide whether federal funds will be used to support research in universities or elsewhere. Sometimes this authority is exercised not only by making funds available but also by placing direct pressure on universities to undertake specific kinds of research. This is the case, for example, when federal officials, primarily those in the Department of Defense, have pressed universities to undertake research not entirely congenial or to assume management responsibilities they would prefer not to have. Finally, the agencies have virtually unlimited discretion to determine the terms and conditions under which research funds will be made available. All in all, the agencies are not entirely passive in the face of cultural forces and forces from within universities.

Productive growth

With all of the reservations that must apply in undertaking to assess causes and effects in a situation as complicated as government-university relations in research, some conclusions seem warranted.

Before stating these, however, the criterion by which the

effects of federal funds can be measured should be explained. One can undertake to weigh the effects of the funds against what the situation might have been if the money had not been provided. This is the standard for assessment in this section of the chapter. In the final section the present state of affairs is assessed against a hypothetical ideal; there the future, rather than developments to date, is the center of attention.

University research in virtually all fields is more extensive, and in most fields of higher average quality, as a result of federal funds. The size and complexity of the total research effort have not stifled the individual.

Faculty members of universities are receiving a great deal of federal money for basic research — basic in the sense that the investigations are not limited to attaining an immediate practical end, and that the scientists are free to pursue their own lines of investigation in a congenial working environment. Certainly, a substantial proportion of the most competent scientists in the country work with the aid of federal funds which permit them to do what they want to do. Basic research is not starved for lack of support; in fact, it is better financed in this country than ever before.

The federal funds have improved the quality of graduate training in the physical and biological sciences. They have also tended to increase the number of graduate students, but other forces have been much more important. Graduate students of exceptional intellectual attainments are probably better trained than ever before, in part because of the existence of federal funds. A sharp cut in these funds would cause the number of graduate students in all physical and biological sciences to decline unless a large federal fellowship program or some other compensatory measure was adopted.

On the other hand, the funds may have tended to decrease the quality of undergraduate instruction, but this is by no means certain.

Federal research funds have beyond any doubt been the most important influence in making the university laboratories of the United States very well equipped, with markedly favorable effects on both the quantity and the quality of research. On the other

211

hand, such gadgeteering and over-concentration on collection of data as may have resulted have been attributable in part, but not entirely, to the federal research funds.

Finally, it seems to me that not only are universities and individual scientists not controlled by the federal government but that their freedom has in many respects been extended by the federal research funds. While the federal government may have, in the words of one observer, "threatened constantly to distort universities by giving more emphasis to applied or developmental than to basic research," [7] a remarkable process of mutual adaptation has kept the threat a potential one.

While these views on the effects of federal funds are subjective, there is wide agreement that research, and universities, are substantially better off with the money than they would have been without it. The dangers of federal domination of science and of pressures towards mediocrity, predicted when federal funds were first made available on a large scale, have for the most part remained potential. When one considers the dangers which have been averted, the financing of university research by the federal government must be judged a success from the viewpoint of both parties.

So far as the future is concerned, the system is imperfect, and potential dangers exist. There is, indeed, no reason to suppose that the slow process of solving the problems created by the federal-university relationships will ever be completed. The government has purposes which are not those of universities. Universities are not in the business of governing, and both government and universities continue to change.

The means of reconciliation

In retrospect, a number of underlying considerations have contributed to a successful solution of the problems generated by the federal funds. These, rather than the direct, current effects of the funds are likely to provide the most useful guides to policy in the future.

The nature of research. The nature of research tends to make the solution of problems in this field less difficult than in some other areas, such as educational policy. As science is international, local traditions, customs, and attitudes are not expected to influence the process and the substance of research. In consequence, there is no tradition that it should be financed and controlled locally. On the contrary, there is a long and strong tradition of conduct and support by the federal government, and a weak tradition of support by state and local governments.[8] For this reason, discussions by university and federal officials are not colored by a general assumption that the federal government should get out and stay out of the business of supporting research.

Research is by nature dynamic. The rate of advance of the substance of science has implications for federal policy — economic, social, and political — that cannot be ignored. Stresses are brought urgently to the surface. They must then be dealt with as concrete, limited, operating problems by the universities and by government.

Breadth of federal authority. The breadth of the missions of federal agencies and the amount of money available to finance research in universities are in many respects a protection to them. Money has been provided for virtually every kind of research. This has tended to reduce the possibility of control by federal agencies. The pressures exerted by individual federal agencies to increase the quantity of research of interest to them have been in large part nullified by the number and variety of pressures from all agencies combined. Similarly, the large number of federal agencies which support work — often work of the same kind — protects science, scientists, and universities. After a period of wavering, the principle of diversity for research support has been adopted as a general policy by the federal government. This principle of operation perpetuates what is unkindly called duplication and overlapping and more charitably called competition in ideas and simultaneous verification. This kind of duplication is abhorrent, however, only to those who value symmetry above productivity. As an English scientist has tartly observed, and with some truth:

It is urgent, for the sake of the welfare of science, that people who worship mere tidiness should occupy themselves in some suitable and congenial occupation and not strive to impose impossible conditions of work on the original scientific investigator.[9]

213

Restricted use of authority. So far as the statutes are concerned, the federal agencies could have imposed virtually any conditions upon universities as a prerequisite to receipt of research funds. The federal agencies had to decide in providing research funds to universities whether the terms and conditions accompanying the money would relate solely to research, or whether an effort would be made to use the funds as a means of securing wise general university policies.

The philosophy that the federal government should decide what is good for universities and then require them to act in the approved manner, or forbid them to act in a disapproved manner, has been expressed in relation to a number of federal research policies. On the ground that secret research has no place in a university, it has been proposed that the federal government should refuse to place contracts involving secret work with them. On the ground that universities should not depend too heavily on the federal government, it has been argued that they should be required to pay part of the cost of research financed by the federal government. On the ground that the loyalties of faculty members will be divided if their salaries are paid by federal agencies, a general policy forbidding the payment of the salaries of faculty members from federal research funds has been advocated.

Even though the policies suggested might be good ones, the federal government should not impose them as a condition for receipt of research funds. Universities have different missions, and what would be good for one might not be desirable for another. The process of taking into protective custody the judgment of universities has no logical end, and removal of the power of decision and ultimate responsibility would weaken them. Finally, the volume of federal funds is so large that any general assumption as to how the universities should act would take on the character of a self-fulfilling prophecy. Universities would tend to become what the executive branch of the federal government says they should be.

The freedom left to universities creates problems for the universities and for the federal government. Some universities may well adopt policies they will later regret. The federal government will, in taking a rather passive role, probably be called to task for failing to see what its shortsighted policies have done, just as it is now common to hear complaints that the government has caused universities to overemphasize applied research. But such problems can be solved, and they are a small price to pay for freedom. On balance the refusal to require universities to adopt general policies that seem appropriate to federal administrators has been one of the most potent reasons underlying the generally satisfactory relations between federal agencies and universities. In this connection, it is useful to recall that the only serious break between the federal agencies and universities developed when the agencies imposed conditions not related to effective performance of research. This was when scientists engaged in nonsecret research had to meet vague "loyalty" and "security" requirements.

Productive guidance. How has it been possible to shift the distribution of research effort across the various spectra — basic to applied, the range of scientific disciplines and the array of scientifically interesting problems — without doing more harm than good?

When the consensus among competent people is that it is desirable to alter research effort, a deliberate attempt to change research patterns can be productive. For example, informed people in this country believe that greater concentration toward the basic end of the research spectrum would be wise at this time. Deliberate efforts to achieve this concentration constitute productive guidance, not control. Conversely, the federal government has not forced a heavy investment in fields before, in I. B. Cohen's apt phrase, "the total scientific situation is ripe." [10] The danger of premature research drives has existed in the form, for example, of demands to set up Manhattan Districts to discover a cure for cancer, and it may exist again. But almost without exception the strong, effective external pressures have been for research in "ripe" fields.

Pressures to shift the emphasis of research must be considered not only in relation to science as an abstraction, but also to scientists as human beings. Sometimes investigators turn from what they would otherwise be doing to undertake a task set for them by a federal agency. Such redirection of effort can be disruptive. A scientist generally has an area of work which absorbs him, which

215

he has grasped, within which he is at home and can wander freely, confidently, and productively. Such persons often have strong intellectual and emotional attachments to their fields, and may well work less effectively if they move in response to external factors. On the other hand, some scientists are stimulated by changing their specialties, or by working on a new problem in concert with congenial persons with acute minds. Moreover, a large volume of federal research funds has been provided under conditions which leave the initiative in seeking funds with the investigator and which permit the direction of research to alter in response to investigators' ideas. All in all, the elements of disruption and of productive stimulus may well balance each other.

Structural adaptations. Structural adaptations in both universities and the federal government have not been mere administrative changes, but an important means of adjusting to the new problems and relationships generated by research.

Within the federal government, new organizations have been created as parts of existing departments or as independent agencies. These organizations reflect recognition that research calls for special administrative structures, procedures and policies. The organizations have been staffed by a new kind of professional federal administrator concerned not with the operation of federal laboratories, but with the provision of research funds to universities. These people typically understand the goals and problems of universities, and of faculty members. In fact, many of them come from universities, and some of them return. The cumulative effect of this rapport between federal and university people on the decision-making process is substantial. One effect is to move discussions from the level of abstraction where doctrine must be invoked as the basis for establishing broad policies. The working relation is based on a series of limited problems to be solved by persons with common professional backgrounds.

The existence of a network of personal relations at various levels in universities and government may be the means of establishing mutual trust and understanding which could further improve communication between them. There appears to be emerging for the first time, a relation between government and universities which parallels the broader rapport existing in Great Britain between the University Grants Committee and the universities. In explaining the singularly smooth and effective operation of this remarkable administrative device, former President Dodds of Princeton pointed out:

> The conclusion is that the success of the University Grants Committee rests fundamentally upon unwritten conventions and personal and social relations of a homogeneous community of university men, in and out of government, who share common tastes and a common outlook unmatched by any similar relationships in the United States.[11]

In this country, similar rapport may be developing not through wearers of the old school tie, but through common professional interests. It would not be wise to idealize the beneficent effect of the relations which now exist. Some representatives of universities condescend to their colleagues in government. Some governmental representatives do not understand the functions and operations of universities. Nevertheless, the relations are becoming more extensive, closer, and more productive.

Not only have the federal agencies changed in structure and function, but a new type of organization — the research center — has been invented to undertake work for which no other laboratories are wholly suitable. These are not normal government laboratories, even though the physical facilities are owned by the federal government and all operating funds are federal. They are not university laboratories in the usual sense, although many of them are associated with universities. They are not industrial laboratories, although many of them are organized and operated like industrial laboratories.

Universities, on the other hand, have adapted themselves structurally to handle the new and extensive tasks created by federal funds. Complicated business affairs have made it necessary to establish special organizations, ranging from sections of existing business offices to research institutes which are in large part autonomous. These offices have been staffed with people who know both university and government business practices. In addition, universities with extensive federal grants and contracts have had to establish means of reviewing at some central point the research that faculty members propose to undertake with federal funds.

217

In short, both universities and federal agencies have adjusted structurally and functionally to rapid and extensive changes. This remarkable adaptability, demonstrated in the face of complex and rapidly changing problems far outweighs the deficiencies of the system and the unsolved problems. It is, in fact, probably the most important single reason why the system has operated reasonably well.

Effective communication. Pressures from society will be exerted on science and they must be exerted without wrecking science. In this vitally important and delicate process of containing social pressures on science, while at the same time stimulating and guiding it towards the service of society, the importance of communication between the worlds of science and politics cannot be overstressed. The persistence of social pressures on science are perhaps the main reason why a sensitive communication between the worlds of science and politics is needed. If scientists and universities do not participate in shaping and directing these pressures, decisions – perhaps unwise ones – will be made for them.

Those acting in a political capacity must impress on the world of science the urgency of social problems to which research can contribute. Conversely, those functioning in a political capacity must be told when fields of study are or are not "ripe," and they must be willing to leave unripe fields fallow. Some of those functioning as scientists must be willing to accommodate to social pressures, and to assist in a realignment of scientific effort when important social goals appear attainable through science.

The administrator and his advisers are in a key position between the world of science and the wider world of social and political needs. One of the most significant tasks of the federal and the university administrators is to adapt science to social pressures while at the same time protecting science against unhealthy social pressures.

Attainment of a workable compromise would be impossible without a sensitive communication system. The problems arising in the search for a workable relation could be solved neither by the agencies, the universities, nor the National Research Council, and the machinery invented and adapted for the task is the scientific advisory group.

The advisory groups, made up largely of scientists from universities, are a new means for deciding whose research will be financed in universities. Many decisions formerly made within single universities have been transferred to faculty members from many universities regrouped by discipline or by research problem. This method of arriving at decisions, which was almost a prerequisite to the successful operation of the system, has shifted important powers of decision from federal administrators and from universities. Both parties have accepted the transfer of power because both have gained much more than they lost.

Scientists throughout the country are well satisfied with the advisory system. Most scientists of stature have some advisory or consulting relation with a federal agency, and consider the function worth while. It gives them, and the scientific disciplines which they represent, a powerful voice in the use of large amounts of research money. The sense of participation felt among university scientists is remarkable.

Apart from the parties immediately concerned, the nation profits from this system. The advisory groups are a means of making the state responsive to the needs of science, rather than the master of science.

Guides to the future

In turning from the past to the future, I assume that the applications of science to practical problems are so powerful and so pervasive that scientists will not be completely independent of the needs of the community. Large amounts of federal money will probably be available for research in universities for the indefinite future. Given this probability, we should not be immobilized by staring fixedly into the eye of the danger of federal control, or other dire consequences of federal support. The wiser course is to consider how the imperative demands of society can be harnessed for the good of science and society, and how an environment can be created to meet the needs of science.

Continuity of policy. Most of the policies and mechanisms

developed over the past decade to deal with federal research in universities are sound. The gradual extension of the degree of freedom given to investigators should continue. The tendency to provide funds in large blocks for research described in general terms should continue. The provision of funds for both basic and applied research from many federal agencies should continue.

The continuation of a sound relation between the federal government and universities, and the removal of some existing difficulties, will be made easier if both parties continue to recognize that their objectives are in part different and that the important questions will be resolved through political processes rather than through technical discussions. The important problems relate to the basic role of the federal government in science, the functions of universities and the functions of university, industrial, and federal laboratories. Not only are important questions of goals and values involved, but a great deal of money is at stake. In this connection, Don Price, who has observed at first hand the operation of the research programs of the Department of Defense, wisely noted that: "Whenever any program requires so much money and involves the fate of so many competing institutions — industrial as well as academic — that program is certain to become loaded with political views." [12]

Many problems will be resolved through mutual accommodation, adjustment to the pressures that each can and will bring to bear to ensure the attainment of vital institutional goals, and adherence by each party to what it considers essential.

Adaptability. Maintenance of the adaptability that has characterized government-university research relations over the past decade is of prime importance because the substance of research will shift and national needs that can be met by research will change. Over long periods of time, the relative urgency of stimulating fundamental as contrasted with basic research may change in this country as it has in others. A recent British report asserted, for example, that the chronic economic difficulties of Great Britain are caused "particularly by the failure to exploit the results of scientific research. While we more than hold our own in fields of pure science, we lag behind other countries in the application of science to the development of new processes." [13] Not only will research change, but the broader question of the role of the federal government in relation to all of the functions of universities will come to the fore. In this connection, the lack of balance between resources for teaching and for research will have to be dealt with, and the role of the federal government in redressing the balance will be a central problem over the years ahead.

Research outside universities. The research centers that were so prominent during and after World War II should be continued and expanded. The centers are uniquely able to carry out certain tasks. More significantly from the point of view of universities, they are a means of avoiding mere bigness. President Stratton of the Massachusetts Institute of Technology has pointed out the implications for universities of the sheer bulk of much modern research:

> New patterns of research are emerging that will be difficult to reconcile with the true spirit of a university. To breach the barriers of knowledge, we have learned the effectiveness of team action backed up by adequate modern equipment . . . If, now, we have discovered a method that is effective, then it is inevitable that it should be developed and expanded. If, in fact, the results of fundamental research are as vital to the national welfare as we have claimed, then we would be lacking in our responsibility if we were to fail to push the organization of scientific research to its ultimate conclusion. This road apparently leads to larger laboratories, a growing costliness of facilities, and an increasing need for the planning of programs.
>
> There is a basic incompatibility between the true spirit of a university and those elements of management which tend to creep into the organization of projects, the planning of programs, and the utilization of costly facilities. One must ask whether the universities can by themselves satisfy the need for all the fundamental research that appears necessary in this country and whether it is wise for them to attempt to do so . . . One must recognize that there may be an ultimate need to establish central institutions to supplement the universities in fundamental research . . . If we strive to contain the widening scope of research entirely within our large universities, we shall end by changing their character and purpose. In so doing, we shall render the greatest possible disservice to the cause of research itself.[14]

In the interest of universities, an increasing proportion of the nation's research, including basic research, should in the future be conducted outside universities in order to sustain the freedom

221

and flexibility of the university environment. For this reason, laboratories outside universities should not be regarded as competitors. They should be viewed as a means whereby the volume of research required in response to irresistible economic, political, and humanitarian forces can be undertaken without forcing universities to undertake inappropriate work.

Unresolved problems

While a reasonably successful reconciliation of the goals of the federal government and of universities has been achieved, and while clear guides to the future exist on some questions, difficult unresolved problems remain. Many questions relating to administrative structures for science are unresolved. More significant problems relate to the effects of federal activities upon the substance of research and on the strength of the nation's educational system.

Structures for research. Despite the remarkable adaptation of structural forms within universities and government to meet the demands of a rapidly expanding national research effort, the lag typical of the adjustment of organizational forms to the tasks imposed upon them exists in universities and in government.

Most universities are still evolving policies and structures which will reconcile the desires and needs of individuals with institutional goals.

Even though the research centers are a means by which pressures on universities to conduct inappropriate large-scale research can be reduced, the centers absorb scientists. Most of the scientists come from universities, and rapid growth of centers can impair the capacity of universities to train the next generation of scientists. For this reason, the rate of growth of centers, their relations to universities, and the nature and extent of their teaching responsibilities comprise one of the most complex and significant problems facing government and universities over the years ahead.

Within the federal government, the fact that there has been no point within the executive branch at which individual universities could present their total needs and resources poses a problem.

Conclusion

More significantly, the executive branch of the federal government has not been organized in a manner which has permitted an effective, continuing examination of the total effects of the research activities of all federal agencies upon higher education. Most of the federal agencies which distribute funds to universities have a research and not a training mission. Even those with a training mission, such as the National Institutes of Health, the Atomic Energy Commission, and the Office of Naval Research, have no statutory authority to concern themselves with the long-run effect of federal research expenditures on higher education in this country. They may do so out of a sense of responsibility, within limits set by law, but the National Science Foundation is the only agency with a clear mandate. The agencies — such as the Department of Defense, the Department of Agriculture, the Atomic Energy Commission, and the National Institutes of Health — which have made the decisions having the greatest effect upon universities are not the places where general federal research policies relating to universities can be formulated.

The National Science Foundation has from its inception recognized the significance of these problems. In 1958, the Foundation produced the most thoughtful report, *Government University Relationships*, yet issued on these matters. The questions need even more sustained and close inquiry.

Apart from studies, the Foundation is already playing a unique and important role in bringing to light and resolving problems relating to education for the sciences at the high school through the graduate school levels. These activities are being extended to make the Foundation an even more effective catalytic agent for bringing individual universities and federal agencies into a relation permitting review of the total effects of the federal programs on the university. Finally, the development of a strong network of advisory groups interested in this problem, including persons in both scientific and administrative positions in universities, could help the Foundation to deal with a major weakness of the entire federal research relation with universities.

At the top, it is important that the preservation of a strong, diversified, free system of universities be viewed as a goal as important as the attainment of the operating objectives of Federal

223

agencies. This attitude should be diffused throughout the agencies and reflected in their actions. At the same time, concern for the vigor and stability of universities should be combined with and tempered by other considerations of equal importance, such as the proper division of federal research among federal laboratories, industrial laboratories, and universities, the relations between strategic military plans and scientific effort, and science in relation to foreign policy.

By moving to the White House responsibility for those aspects of national science policy that are effectively dealt with centrally and by emphasizing the responsibilities of the National Science Foundation for the promotion of basic research and for education in the sciences (Executive Order 10,807, March 13, 1959), the President strengthened the structure for dealing with the effects of federal research on universities. The structure was further strengthened by reconstituting the President's Science Advisory Committee as a group of nongovernmental advisers reporting directly to him. The appointment of the Special Assistant to the President for Science and Technology was another important step. Finally, the problem of securing coherent policies among the agencies was attacked by the establishment of the Federal Council for Science and Technology. Significantly, an answer was not sought through recommending the establishment of a Department of Science, a proposal made periodically since 1884, and most recently in 1958 as S.3126, a Bill to Create a Department of Science and Technology.[15] Science should not be centralized, but should continue to remain diffused throughout the federal establishment. Moreover, problems of policy relating to the whole executive branch can be dealt with most effectively not in departments but in the Executive Office of the President.

While the federal structure continues to evolve toward a stronger, more solidly based and logically articulated machine, I think that additional steps will eventually prove desirable. The establishment of administrative devices through executive order lacks the sanction of Congress, and those characteristics of the Executive Office of the President which are most enduring are those established by statute. The next step in the evolution of a fully adequate structure for science policy at the top of the executive branch might therefore be the establishment by statute of a science and technology office in the Executive Office of the President. This organization might well be analogous in structure and function to the Council of Economic Advisers. Such a group would have the proper status, and it would be an enduring part of the Executive Office of the President. The establishment of a Congressional Joint Committee on Science and Technology, analogous to the Joint Committee on Atomic Energy, would further strengthen the total federal structure for dealing with science.

Since a statutory Council for Science and Technology would in a certain sense be a part of the executive branch of government, the need for vigorous, independent criticism of the scientific policies of the Federal government would become even more important. This role is one which might be played most effectively by the National Academy of Sciences–National Research Council.

The federal structure for science policy is much stronger than it was a decade ago, and adaptation is proceeding at a reasonable rate. The years since World War II may well be viewed in the future as a period when activities of the government relating to research in universities grew at an extremely rapid rate, and somewhat at random. Over the next decade the affairs of federal agencies and those of universities will become more closely intertwined. The adaptation of structure will have to continue if the problems generated thereby are to be solved reasonably well.

Substance of research. Structures should be designed for the effective performance of functions, and the most significant unresolved problems relate to the substance of research and education rather than to the administrative forms.

While basic research is now better supported than ever before, gaps exist because some important investigations are outside the area of interest of any agency except the National Science Foundation. For example, investigators of high competence in such areas as bioluminescence, archaeology, meteorology, pure mathematics, linguistics, astronomy and radio astronomy, field studies in biology, and geology have received inadequate support. In addition, science has evolved over the past few years in a manner emphasizing needs for larger and expensive physical facilities for basic research. Not only in nuclear physics, but in such fields as

225

oceanography, meteorology, and materials research, large new research equipment is needed. There is little prospect of filling these glaring gaps without substantial aid from the federal government.

An important task of the National Science Foundation in supporting research is to provide money to promising scientists and promising ideas in neglected fields of science, and those fields whose relevance to the solution of practical problems is not obvious are most likely to be neglected. This task is not solely support of general-purpose basic research, even if the term were operationally usable, but the wider one of filling any kind of gap that may appear in basic science. For example, analytical engineering — the sophisticated scrutiny of available knowledge to determine what kinds of "things" can be built and what can be invented with existing knowledge — has been inadequately supported.

Looking ahead, extension of the postwar progress in securing support for basic research is important. In this connection, the National Science Foundation's budgets for support of research have been skimpy until fiscal year 1959, when the budget of the Foundation was almost tripled to a level of $140 million. Over the period 1953 through 1957 the Foundation has been able to support only 28 percent of the $140 million requested.[16] While such statistics must be viewed cautiously, work in some fields has suffered because of inadequate financial support.

At the same time, it should be borne in mind that lack of money is not now the most important barrier to the establishment of greater national strength in basic research. The more acute problems relate to the training of manpower, the effects of heavy research support upon universities as educational institutions, and the terms and conditions under which federal funds are distributed to them.

With respect to all kinds of research, the terms and conditions under which federal funds are provided to university scientists should be further improved. Funds are still dependent upon year-to-year appropriations which may fluctuate sharply. A productive next step would be to place research and development appropriations on a two- to five-year instead of a one-year basis. Much federal money is still provided for research that sets narrow research tasks and requires specific performance from the investigators. Here, it is useful to recall that the obligation of the federal agencies is not to meet the full wishes of the universities. A degree of incompatibility between the objectives of the agencies and universities is built into the system because the agencies have functions that are not necessarily best discharged by acting in a way most congenial to universities. They may adapt their policies to the extent that maintenance of strong universities is a governmental concern compatible with attainment of the direct governmental objectives. Within these limits, the agencies do have an obligation, thus far imperfectly met, to concern themselves with the strength of universities.

Education and research

The interrelated tasks of training and using manpower, strengthening of our total educational structure for the production of scientists, and fostering the development of highly talented students are emerging as functions that are as significant to the nation as support of research.

The critically important problems of training enough scientists well and of using them well are far from resolved. The support of scientific training provided as a by-product of support of research has been useful, but fortuitous and not entirely satisfactory. A much wider federal scholarship and fellowship program is needed to ensure that no talent remains untrained. This need was met in part by enactment of the National Defense Education Act in 1958. In addition, the status of the large group of professional nonfaculty scientists loosely attached to universities should be improved. But there appears to be no way of using this talented group more effectively until universities have enough money to hire them as faculty members.

The federal research funds have affected not only research in universities, but all their functions. For the long run, the effects of the funds on the educational functions of universities may be more significant than their effects on research. Such unresolved questions as these remain:

How are universities to exert countervailing forces against the pressure to expand the physical sciences?

227

What are the implications of an expanding volume of research for the capacity of universities to teach the impending wave of students?

How are universities to attract and keep teachers with research talent in the face of competition from industry, financed in substantial part by federal money?

How are universities to withstand the temptation to accept federal funds which would over the long run divert them from their central functions?

If federal research funds pose a threat to the freedom of universities, the primary threat is that universities will not find satisfactory answers to questions such as these, rather than that bureaucrats will exercise arbitrary authority.

There is, finally, the difficult question of general federal aid for the financing of universities. This is related to federal aid to research for two reasons. First, such aid is already being provided indirectly and in unmeasurable amounts from research funds through such channels as provision of equipment inevitably and properly used for teaching, provision of income (often including partial or total payment of salaries) to teachers, and payment of the full costs of research. Since the role of the federal government in supporting higher education is traditionally a subject for heated debate, it is remarkable that the significant Federal payments to higher education derived from research funds have not been more vigorously argued. The discussion has been muted because the support has been piecemeal, dispersed among a number of Federal agencies, and a by-product of the less debatable function of aiding research. Second, the question of general aid to universities arises in a more significant form in relation to the need of the nation not only for a strong system for producing scientists but also for a system able to educate citizens for a democracy in times of unprecedented change and challenge.

So far as capital expenditures are concerned, the nation's entire system of higher education is underbuilt and underequipped. The Special Assistant to the President for Science and Technology, Dr. James R. Killian, pointed out early in 1959 that:

Of the 700 colleges and universities in the United States which offer graduate degrees, something less than 300 offer graduate degrees in scientific, medical, and engineering subjects, and not enough of these can claim real distinction in any one scientific field. The few top-quality departments are in danger of becoming overloaded, and the peak in graduate enrollment is still several years off. It is especially important that we build more first-rate graduate schools of engineering and that they be developed in close association with excellent departments of science.[17]

It will require hundreds of millions of dollars for capital construction to meet existing and emerging educational needs. Part of the needs will be met by private gifts and by state appropriations. But unless trends in state support and private giving are sharply reversed, some form of general federal aid for construction will also be required if the problem is to be solved in time. Apart from fiscal questions, which are not to be ignored, there is ample precedent in the activities of a number of federal agencies for the policies which are necessary to provide federal funds for construction of educational and research facilities without impairing the freedom of universities.

Whether federal aid for the general operating costs of universities will be required is not relevant here, but the research experience is relevant to the question whether it would be possible to provide federal funds for education without introducing federal control. The threats to the freedom of universities encountered in providing general aid would be much the same as those encountered in providing research aid, for teaching and research are inextricably interwoven. The research experience leads me to the conclusion that, if general federal aid for higher education will be required, the possibility that funds can be provided without restricting the freedom of universities is bright. The general federal research policies point the way. These include the development of a sound set of guiding principles with extensive help from nongovernmental advisory groups, a pragmatic administrative approach, maintenance of diverse sources of support, and powerful sources of independent, responsible criticism.

Values

Underlying all of the specific unresolved problems relating to government-university relations are the cultural values and pressures that have played such an important role since World War

229

II. These will continue to exercise a dominant influence on the policies of both government and universities. Those facets of our national culture which have in the past militated against intellectual excellence as a paramount goal will probably change slowly because they are so deeply ingrained. Until learning of all kinds and exploration of the unknown in all fields are more widely respected as ends in themselves, social pressures will be exerted away from rather than toward intellectual excellence. The attitudes which together comprise a national judgment that intellectual excellence is not highly admirable are firmly embedded. They affect the tone of government and every level of education. They can be altered only slowly, and only by extraordinarily strong forces.

Attitudes toward secondary education must change. This involves general willingness to do the things — such as raising salaries and lifting the intellectual standards required of teachers — that are necessary to attract a higher proportion of highly intelligent people as secondary school teachers, and to spend the required billions. Changes of this kind are not easily brought about. As Archibald MacLeish has pointed out, "a radical change in educational policy cannot be ordered as an automobile manufacturer orders a new model. When it comes, it will come out of a change in the community's conception of itself." [18]

Widespread attitudes toward the functions of higher education must also change. In this connection a perceptive report of the Carnegie Foundation for the Advancement of Teaching has observed that:

> One would like to believe that Congressmen, the heads of Federal agencies, and others concerned with Federal action in higher education will be guided by something approaching a philosophy of higher education and a sense of its role in American society. This could occur only through the vigorous and enlightened action of America's leaders in higher education . . . Now the truth is that measured against this challenge, public understanding of American higher education leaves much to be desired. And it must be admitted that this is partly the fault of our educational leaders.[19]

Part of the problem is that some universities, reflecting important aspects of our society, do not establish an environment where intellectual excellence is valued most highly. A university system closer to the ideal of a company of scholars engaged in creation, transmission, and preservation of knowledge would involve a change in the tone, the values, the rigor, and the intellectual discipline of many universities.

The most important prerequisite to the establishment of a stronger university system and to the achievement of other national goals in education and science is the strength of the national will to give first place to education at all levels, and to the fostering of excellence in all fields.

Appendix

Section 1. Tables

Table A-1. Relation between gross national product and total national research and development expenditures, 1930–1957 (millions of dollars)

Year	Gross national product [a]	Total national expenditures [b]	Expenditures/gross national product
1930	91,000	166	0.20
1935	72,000	190	.25
1940	101,000	350	.35
1945	214,000	2,041	1.00
1950	285,000	2,503	0.90
1955	391,000	6,280	1.60
1956	412,000	6,970	1.70
1957	437,000	10,000	2.30

[a] Council of Economic Advisors, *Economic Report of the President, January 1959*, 117.
[b] Estimates for years before 1955 are from a National Science Foundation mimeographed staff document prepared for the Conference on the Economic Effects of Research, Washington, D.C., 9 February 1954.

Table A-2. Distribution of federal research and development obligations among major groups of laboratories, 1952–1959 [a] (millions of dollars)

Fiscal year	Laboratories receiving funds							
	Total		Federal		Industrial		Nonprofit	
	Amount	Percent	Amount	Percent	Amount	Percent	Amount	Percent
1952	1,816	100	378	21	1,100	60	338	19
1953	2,810	100	970	34	1,520	54	330	12
1954	2,586	100	957	37	1,371	53	310	12
1955	2,739	100	958	35	1,452	53	329	12
1956	2,419	100	1,095	45	962	51	363	12
1957	2,724	100	1,280	47	978	36	466	18
1958	3,104	100	1,360	44	1,188	38	556	18
1959	3,545	100	1,320	37	1,613	45	612	18

[a] Figures for Government, industrial, and nonprofit laboratories in 1951 and 1952 are derived from *Federal Funds for Science*, vol. 1, p. 36, vol. 2, p. 5, and vol. 5, p. 47. The three-way

distribution for 1953 is based on *Reviews of Data on Research and Development*, No. 1, December 1956. The three-way distribution for later years based on *Federal Funds for Science*, vol. 5, pp. 45 and 47, vol. 6, pp. 53 and 55, and vol. 7, pp. 68, 71, and 74. Only the funds for nonprofit institutions are reasonably accurate in all years. The distribution of federal funds between government laboratories and industrial laboratories for the years 1951 and 1952 was poorly estimated. The sharp proportionate increase shown for federal laboratories in 1953 is not a real increase, but the result of refined estimates.

Table A-3. Federal research funds to educational institutions compared with funds to all nonprofit institutions, 1952–1958 (millions of dollars)

Fiscal year		Nonprofit institutions	
	Total amount	Educational Amount	Percent
1952 [a]	338	276	80
1953 [b]	330	280	85
1954 [c]	310	260	84
1955 [c]	329	275	84
1956 [d]	363	310	86
1957 [d]	466	377	81
1958 [d]	556	450	81
1959 [d]	612	496	81

[a] Data for 1952 from *Federal Funds for Science*, vol. 1, p. 32. Figures adjusted to exclude approximately $20 million for increase in research and development funds from the National Science Foundation.
[b] Data for 1953 from *Reviews of Data on Research and Development*, no. 1, December 1956.
[c] Data for 1954 and 1955, derived primarily from percentage distribution of obligations applied to total federal expenditures, since only obligations are reported to NSF by performance component. The percentage of funds transferred to educational institutions in 1954 was assumed to be the same as in 1955, *Federal Funds for Science*, vol. 5, pp. 30–41.
[d] Data for 1956 from *Federal Funds for Science*, vol. 6, pp. 53 and 55, and for 1957, 1958, and 1959 from *Federal Funds for Science*, vol. 7, pp. 68, 71, and 74.

Table A-4. Obligations to educational institutions compared with total estimated federal research and development obligations, by administering agency, 1959 (millions of dollars)

Agency	Total	Educational institutions	
		Amount	Percent of total
Total	3,545	496	14
Department of Defense	2,450 [a]	178 [b]	7
Air Force	(828)	(50)	(6)
Navy	(682)	(58)	(8)
Army	(512)	(60)	(11)
Atomic Energy Commission	546	166	30
Department of Health, Education and Welfare	185	79	43
Department of Agriculture	113	30	27
National Science Foundation	43	38	90
All other agencies [c]	208	5	2

Source: National Science Foundation, *Federal Funds for Science*, vol. 7, pp. 72–74.
[a] Includes $428,000,000 in departmentwide funds allocated among the services.
[b] Includes $10,000,000 in departmentwide funds allocated among the services.
[c] Reconstruction Finance Corporation, Department of Commerce, Veterans Administration, National Advisory Committee for Aeronautics, Tennessee Valley Authority, Department of Interior, Department of State, Federal Civil Defense Administration, National Security Resources Board (later Office of Defense Mobilization), Department of Labor, Housing, and Home Finance Agency, and Library of Congress.

Appendix

Table A-5. Federal funds for support of the research of individual faculty members,
by administering agency, 1959 (millions of dollars)

Agency	Support of individuals	
	Amount	Percent
Total	296	100
Department of Defense	108 [a]	36
Air Force	(43)	(14)
Navy	(44)	(15)
Army	(21)	(7)
Atomic Energy Commission	37	13
Department of Health, Education, and Welfare	79	27
Department of Agriculture	30	10
National Science Foundation	38	13
All other agencies	4	1

Source: National Science Foundation, Federal Funds for Science, vol. 7, pp. 72–74.
[a] Includes $10,000,000 in departmentwide funds allocated among the services.

Table A-6. Federal research grants and contracts (excluding funds for research centers) as a
percentage of operating budgets of large universities, 1954 (millions of dollars)[a]

Universities grouped by descending size of operating budget	Total operating budget	Federal research grants and contracts	
		Amount	Percent of operating budget
First 10	386	63	16.4
First 15	496	71	14.4
First 25	664	90	14.4

[a] These unpublished data were supplied by the National Science Foundation and the Office of
Education, Department of Health, Education and Welfare. See also the President's Committee
on Education beyond the High School, *Second Report to the President* (Washington: Government
Printing Office, 1957), p. 77. "Organized research" is reported as 12.9 percent of "current expenditures" of United States colleges and universities in 1953–54.

Table A-7. Federal and nonfederal sources of support for university
research, 1953–54 (millions of dollars)

Field	Total	Federal	Nonfederal		
			Total	University	Other
		Absolute figures			
All fields	$206	$142	$63.8	$17.5	$46.3
Life sciences	66	34	32.9	7.6	25.3
Physical sciences	56	47	8.0	2.5	5.5
Chemistry	(15)	(10)	(4.3)	(0.7)	(3.6)
Physics	(23)	(22)	(0.9)	(0.4)	(0.5)
Mathematics	(7)	(6)	(0.4)	(0.2)	(0.2)
Other	(11)	(9)	(2.4)	(1.2)	(1.2)
Engineering	63	52	11.2	3.4	7.8
Psychology	7	5	1.5	0.6	0.9
Social sciences	12	3	9.2	3.0	6.2
All others	2	1	1.0	0.4	0.6

235

Table A-7 (continued)

Field	Total	Federal	Nonfederal Total	University	Other
		Percentage distribution among fields			
All fields	100	100	100	100	100
Life sciences	32	24	52	43	55
Physical sciences	27	33	12	15	12
Chemistry	(7)	(7)	(7)	(4)	(8)
Physics	(11)	(16)	(1)	(3)	(1)
Mathematics	(3)	(4)	(0)	(1)	(0)
Other	(6)	(6)	4	(7)	(3)
Engineering	31	37	18	20	17
Psychology	3	3	2	3	2
Social sciences	6	2	15	17	13
All other	1	1	1	2	1
		Percentage distribution within fields			
All fields	100	69	31	9	22
Life sciences	100	50	50	12	38
Physical sciences	100	86	14	4	10
Chemistry	100	70	30	6	24
Physics	100	96	4	2	2
Mathematics	100	94	6	3	3
Other	100	80	20	10	10
Engineering	100	82	18	6	12
Psychology	100	76	24	9	15
Social sciences	100	25	75	23	52
All other	100	50	50	20	30

Source: National Science Foundation, *Scientific Activities for Research and Development in Colleges and Universities — Expenditures and Manpower, 1953–1954* (Washington: Government Printing Office, 1959).

Table A-8. Nonfederal support for university research, 1953–54 (millions of dollars)

Field	Total	University funds	Foundations	Industry	Private gifts	All other
		Absolute figures				
All fields	$63.8	$17.5	$22.7	$18.6	$4.1	$0.9
Life sciences	32.9	7.5	15.8	6.3	2.8	0.4
Physical sciences	8.0	2.5	1.4	3.4	0.5	0.1
Chemistry	(4.3)	(0.7)	(1.0)	(2.5)	0.1	(0)
Physics	(0.9)	(0.4)	(0.2)	(0.2)	0.1	(0)
Mathematics	(0.4)	(0.2)	(0.1)	(0.1)	0	(0)
Other	(2.4)	(1.2)	(0.2)	(0.6)	0.2	(0)
Engineering	11.2	3.4	0.5	7.0	0.2	0.1
Psychology	1.5	0.6	0.8	0.1	0.1	0
Social sciences	9.2	3.0	4.1	1.4	0.5	0.3
All other	1.0	0.5	0.1	0.4	0	0

Appendix

Field	Total	University funds	Founda-tions	Indus-try	Private gifts	All other
Percentage distribution among fields						
All fields	100	100	100	100	100	100
Life sciences	52	43	70	34	69	45
Physical sciences	12	15	6	18	12	6
Chemistry	(7)	(4)	(4)	(13)	(3)	(1)
Physics	(1)	(3)	(1)	(1)	(2)	(0)
Mathematics	(0)	(1)	(0)	(1)	(1)	(0)
Other	(4)	(7)	(1)	(3)	(6)	(5)
Engineering	18	20	2	37	5	15
Psychology	2	3	3	1	2	4
Social sciences	15	17	18	8	11	30
All other	1	2	1	2	1	—
Percentage distribution within fields						
All fields	100	27	36	29	7	1
Life sciences	100	23	48	19	9	1
Physical sciences:	100					
Chemistry	100	16	23	58	3	0
Physics	100	50	22	18	10	0
Mathematics	100	52	14	26	8	0
Other	100	52	7	28	11	2
Engineering	100	31	4	62	2	1
Psychology	100	36	50	7	5	2
Social sciences	100	32	45	15	5	3
All other	100	44	14	37	5	0

Source: National Science Foundation, *Scientific Activities for Research and Development in Colleges and Universities — Expenditures and Manpower, 1953–1954* (Washington: Government Printing Office, 1959).

Table A-9. Concentration of federal research funds among universities, 1953–54 [a]

Volume of research grants and contracts	Number of institutions	Amount (millions of dollars)	Percent	Cumulative percent
All institutions	173	141.6	100	0
$10 million and over	1	16.9	12	12
$5 million to $10 million	5	30.4	21	33
$3 million to $5 million	8	31.4	22	55
$1 million to $3 million	22	36.2	26	81
$0.5 million to $1 million	18	12.7	9	90
$0.25 to $0.5 million	18	6.5	5	95
$0.1 million to $.25 million	32	5.2	4	99
Under $0.1 million	69	2.3	1	100

Source: National Science Foundation, *Scientific Activities for Research and Development in Colleges and Universities — Expenritures and Manpower, 1953–1954* (Washington: Government Printing Office, 1959).
[a] Exclusive of funds for operation of research centers.

Table A-10. Percentage distribution of Ph.D.'s by field, selected years, 1926–1957

Field	1926–1930	1936–1940	1946–1950	1956–1957
All fields	100.0	100.0	100.0	100.0
Natural sciences	44.2	47.6	38.3	31.7
Chemistry	(16.8)	(17.2)	(15.1)	(11.4)
Physical science	(8.5)	(8.7)	(8.5)	(5.4)
Earth science	(4.0)	(2.8)	(2.6)	(1.7)
Biological science	(14.6)	(18.9)	(11.7)	(12.6)
Other	(0)	(0)	(0.4)	(0.6)
Applied biology	1.5	2.2	4.8	3.8
Agriculture	(1.5)	(2.2)	(4.5)	(3.3)
Home economics	(0)	(0)	(0.3)	(0.5)
Engineering	1.7	2.1	5.6	6.8
Social science	16.9	15.2	13.1	12.5
Economics	(6.6)	(4.8)	(3.8)	(2.7)
History	(5.7)	(5.3)	(4.2)	(3.6)
Other	(4.6)	(5.1)	(5.1)	(6.2)
Psychology	4.6	4.1	4.1	6.3
Humanities and Arts	17.1	17.9	15.3	10.3
English	(5.5)	(6.2)	(4.1)	(4.0)
Language	(5.8)	(6.8)	(3.1)	(2.5)
Philosophy	(5.4)	(4.1)	(4.6)	(1.0)
Fine arts	(0.4)	(0.8)	(3.5)	(2.8)
Health fields	0	0.5	1.0	1.7
Business and Commerce	0	0	0.7	1.1
Education	13.4	9.9	14.2	17.5
Other	0.6	0.5	2.9	8.3
Law	(0.6)	(0.4)	(0.5)	(0.4)
Miscellaneous [a]	(0)	(0.1)	(2.4)	(7.9)

Source: 1956–1957. U.S. Department of Health, Education and Welfare, Office of Education, *Earned degrees conferred by educational institutions, 1956–1957*, Circular no. 527 (Washington: Government Printing Office, 1958), pp. 9–13; all years before 1956. D. Wolfle, *America's resources of specialized talent* (New York: Harper & Brothers, 1954), pp. 298–299.
[a] Architecture, journalism, library science and social work.

Table A-11. Ph.D. and M.D. degrees granted annually in the United States, selected years, 1930–1955

Year	Total Number	Total Index	All Ph.D.'s Number	All Ph.D.'s Index	All M.D.'s Number	All M.D.'s Index
1930	6,781	100	2,216	100	4,565	100
1940	8,387	123	3,290	150	5,097	111
1945	7,102	104	1,966	90	5,136	112
1950	11,886	175	6,633	300	5,553	122
1955	15,835	232	8,900	400	6,935	152

Source: National Science Foundation, Trends in the Employment and Training of Scientists and Engineers (Washington: Government Printing Office, May 1956), Chart 2, and *Journal of the American Medical Association 168*, 1598 (1958).

Appendix

Table A-12. Distribution of graduate students in the United States, by field, 1954

Field	Number	Percent
Total	217,000	100
Science and engineering	52,500	25
Life sciences	14,500	7
Biology	(10,700)	(5)
Agriculture and medicine	(3,800)	(2)
Physical sciences	19,000	9
Mathematics	(3,400)	(1)
Physics	(4,900)	(3)
Chemistry	(7,800)	(4)
Other	(2,900)	(1)
Engineering	19,000	9
Other fields	164,500	75
Social sciences	26,500	12
Nonsciences	138,000	63
Education	(93,000)	(42)
Other	(45,000)	(21)

Source: National Science Foundation, *Graduate Student Enrollment and Support in American Universities and Colleges, 1954* (Washington: Government Printing Office, 1957), p. 2. Absolute figures adjusted upward on the assumption that the following proportions of graduate students were covered by the survey: physical sciences, 100 percent; life sciences, 100 percent; engineering and social sciences, 80 percent; education and other, 68 percent. Completeness of coverage estimated by National Science Foundation staff.

Table A-13. Aptitude test score distributions of students in different fields, 1947

	Percentile scores		
Field	10	50	90
	Natural sciences and engineering		
Natural sciences:			
Graduate students	113	128	142
Ph.D.'s	117	133	153
Chemistry:			
Graduate students	113	129	143
Ph.D.'s	120	135	152
Other physical sciences:			
Graduate students	117	131	143
Ph.D.'s	118	138	156
Biological sciences:			
Graduate students	112	126	140
Ph.D.'s	115	129	145
Engineering:			
Graduate students	113	126	140
Ph.D.'s	116	133	148

Table A-13 (continued)

Field	10	50	90
		Percentile scores	
		Other fields	
Psychology:			
Graduate students	118	132	144
Ph.D.'s	120	137	158
Social sciences [a]	109	124	140
Humanities and arts	110	125	141
Medicine	114	127	140
Business and commerce	107	121	135
Education	107	121	133

Source: D. Wolfle, *America's Resources of Specialized Talent* (New York: Harper, 1954), pp. 317–322.
[a] The following figures are all for graduate students because data for Ph.D.'s are not available.

Table A-14. Extent to which largest graduate schools grant Ph.D.'s in selected scientific fields

Universities [a]	Bacteriology [b]	Biochemistry [c]	Biology [d]	Chemistry [e]	Physics [f]
California	X	X	X	X	X
Chicago		X		X	X
Illinois	X			X	
Harvard			X	X	X
Michigan	X			X	X
Columbia		X		X	X
N. Y. U.			X		X
Ohio State	X	X		X	X
Wisconsin	X	X		X	X

Source: Office of Education, *Earned Degrees Conferred by Higher Educational Institutions, 1955–56*, circular 461 (Washington: Government Printing Office, 1957).
[a] 9 universities granting 36 percent of all Ph.D.'s.
[b] 9 universities granting 50 percent of Ph.D.'s in bacteriology.
[c] 12 universities granting 66 percent of Ph.D.'s in biochemistry.
[d] 12 universities granting 66 percent of Ph.D.'s in biology.
[e] 19 universities granting 75 percent of Ph.D.'s in chemistry.
[f] 19 universities granting 64 percent of Ph.D.'s in physics.

Table A-15. Number and percent of respondents, by departments

Department	Number			Percent responding		
	Total	Respond-ing	Not re-sponding	Total	Public	Private
Total	191	100	91	52	57	45
Chemistry [a]	50	24	26	45	47	43
Biology	15	9	6	60	100	33
Physics	39	19	20	49	55	45
Engineering	14	8	6	57	60	51
Psychology	31	16	15	51	50	60
Mathematics	22	12	10	54	50	60
Bacteriology	13	8	5	62	70	40
Geology	7	4	3	100	100	100

Source: Based on questionnaire in Appendix, Section 2.
[a] Including biochemistry.

Appendix

Table A-16. Percent of Ph.D.'s awarded represented by respondents, 1955

Department	Total Ph.D. degrees awarded in the U.S.	Ph.D. degrees by responding departments	Percent represented by respondents
Total	3,635	1,035	28
Chemistry and Biochemistry	1,152	261	23
Engineering	599	144	24
Physics	511	146	29
Psychology	688	237	34
Bacteriology	131	45	34
Mathematics	250	91	35
Geology	154	55	36
Biology	150	56	37

Source: Based on questionnaire in Appendix, Section 2.

Table A-17. Reported changes in the quality of graduate training, 1946–1957

Changes in quality of training	Percent reporting given change		
	Total	Deans	Dep't Heads
Total	100	100	100
Increased markedly	24	22	25
Increased somewhat	47	54	45
Decreased somewhat	11	10	11
Decreased markedly	—	—	—
Remained the same	13	10	14
No response	5	4	5

Source: Based on questionnaire in Appendix, Section 2.

Section 2. Questionnaire

In this section are presented the questionnaire form from which data given in Chapter 7 were drawn, and certain data relating to the responses to the questionnaire.

Effects of Federal Research Funds in Universities on the Training of Graduate Students
(A Study by C. V. Kidd, December, 1956)

Introductory Note

Listed on the following pages are the factors which seem to be most frequently mentioned when the effects of federal research funds on the training of graduate students are discussed. These factors are stated as questions in an attempt to save your time. If you think the questions miss the point, or are otherwise inadequate, I would be pleased if you would write some brief comments on what you think the important judgments are.

In answering just underline the appropriate word, or check the appropriate space.

Three important notes:

a. All of the questions relate not to your college or university, but your field in the country as a whole.

b. The effect of federal research contracts and grants and not federal fellowships, G. I. payments, or other sources of federal money is sought.

c. The questions could have been placed in a more compact format. The length is designed to make the job of answering easier and quicker.

d. The questions are phrased simply not because the phenomena under observation are simple, but because this seems the only practical way to get net impressions. Please expand your response if you feel that a summary answer inadequately expresses your opinion.

I (am willing, not willing) to have my response identified with me in any preliminary or published report.

Please send me a copy of the preliminary analysis of the returns.

_____
Signature

_____
Signature

Note: If you do not have sufficient confidence in your assessment of the training of all graduate students in your field for the country as a whole, please indicate the group that you do feel competent to assess:

These responses relate to:

_____ My department
_____ My geographical region
_____ Large universities
Other (specify)

Section I. Net Assessment

1. Has the average quality of training received by *all graduate students in your field for the country as a whole* increased, decreased, or remained the same over the past decade?

_____ Increased markedly
_____ Increased somewhat
_____ Decreased somewhat
_____ Decreased markedly
_____ Remained the same

Comment:

2. If the quality of training has changed, what part have federal research funds played in bringing about the change?

      _____ Federal research funds primarily responsible for change

      _____ Federal research funds partially responsible

      _____ Federal research funds unrelated to change

      _____ Change occurred in spite of influence of Federal funds

Comment:

3. As contrasted with all students, how have the federal research funds affected the quality of the training of the few students potentially capable of highly creative profound work of the highest caliber in your field.

      _____ Adversely, as compared with all students

      _____ Favorably, as compared with all students

      _____ Same as all students

Comment:

4. What has been the net effect of all three of the above factors combined?

      _____ Good

      _____ Adverse

      _____ Neutral

And how significant has this effect been?

      _____ Striking

      _____ Substantial

      _____ Unimportant

5. How have federal research funds affected the following factors influencing the quality of graduate training?

      (Where no effect is checked, do not answer the two additional subquestions)

If factor affects quality the effect is:

	Very important	*Significant*	*Unimportant*
A. Availability of faculty for graduate teaching:			
(No effect _____)			
Increased _____	_____	_____	_____
Decreased _____	_____	_____	_____
B. Teaching capacity of individual faculty members:			
(No effect _____)			
Increased _____	_____	_____	_____
Decreased _____	_____	_____	_____

	Very important	Significant	Unimportant

C. Breadth and duration of training
in fundamentals:

    (No effect _____)

	Very important	Significant	Unimportant
Better training	_____	_____	_____
Less adequate training	_____	_____	_____

D. Absorption of students in graduate study:

    (No effect _____)

	Very important	Significant	Unimportant
More complete absorption	_____	_____	_____
Less complete absorption	_____	_____	_____

E. Availability of data for teaching and dissertations:

    (No effect _____)

	Very important	Significant	Unimportant
Net positive contribution	_____	_____	_____
Net detriment	_____	_____	_____

F. Availability of instruments and
tools:

    (No effect _____)

	Very important	Significant	Unimportant
Net positive contribution	_____	_____	_____
Net detriment	_____	_____	_____

G. Total supply of university
teachers:

    (No effect _____)

	Very important	Significant	Unimportant
Net gain in number and quality of faculty	_____	_____	_____
Net harm through losses to in- dustry and research centers	_____	_____	_____

6. If you believe either that the average quality of graduate training in your field has decreased for the country as a whole or that the quality of training of some students in some institutions has fallen, please express judgments as to the effect of —

Appendix

	Very important	Significant	Unimportant	Nonexistent

A. Pressure on faculty towards acceptance of research funds for research providing poor training opportunities. This pressure exerted by:

	Very important	Significant	Unimportant	Nonexistent
Federal agencies	⎯⎯	⎯⎯	⎯⎯	⎯⎯
University officials	⎯⎯	⎯⎯	⎯⎯	⎯⎯
Other (Specify)				

B. Characteristics of faculty leading to deterioration of training:

	Very important	Significant	Unimportant	Nonexistent
Over-absorption in own research	⎯⎯	⎯⎯	⎯⎯	⎯⎯
Expansionist attitudes	⎯⎯	⎯⎯	⎯⎯	⎯⎯
Other (Specify)				

C. Poor institutional guide lines for development of graduate students:

	Very important	Significant	Unimportant	Nonexistent
Inadequate planning of income producing and academic work	⎯⎯	⎯⎯	⎯⎯	⎯⎯
Inadequate means of adjusting work to needs of individuals	⎯⎯	⎯⎯	⎯⎯	⎯⎯
Other (Specify)				

D. Size and characteristics of universities leading to:

	Very important	Significant	Unimportant	Nonexistent
Greater uniformity of thought	⎯⎯	⎯⎯	⎯⎯	⎯⎯
Pressure for conformity	⎯⎯	⎯⎯	⎯⎯	⎯⎯
Other (Specify)				

On balance, these observed adverse effects are attributable primarily to:

⎯⎯ (A) Pressure on faculty
⎯⎯ (B) Characteristics of faculty
⎯⎯ (C) Poor institutional guide lines
⎯⎯ (D) Size and characteristics of universities
⎯⎯ Combinations of (A), (B), (C), and (D)
⎯⎯ Specify:

General Observations

1. What would be the effect on graduate students in your field in terms of numbers if federal research funds for all fields of study were —

Sharply cut back?
_____ Sharp reduction
_____ Moderate reduction
_____ No effect

Substantially increased?
_____ Sharp increase
_____ Moderate increase
_____ No effect

Remarks on reasons for your responses:

2. What would be the effect on graduate students in your field *in terms of quality* of the group if federal research funds for all fields of study were —

Sharply cut back?
_____ Marked increase in quality
_____ Moderate increase in quality
_____ No effect
_____ Moderate decrease in quality
_____ Marked decrease in quality

Substantially increased?
_____ Marked increase in quality
_____ Moderate increase in quality
_____ No effect
_____ Moderate decrease in quality
_____ Marked decrease in quality

Remarks on reasons for your responses:

3. What has been the effects of Federal funds on research in your field for the country as a whole —

On quality?
_____ Marked increase
_____ Some increase
_____ No effect
_____ Some decrease
_____ Marked decrease

On quantity?
_____ Marked decrease
_____ Some decrease
_____ No effect
_____ Some increase
_____ Marked increase

On lines of investigation?
_____ No effect
_____ Harmful bias; some fields slighted
_____ Harmful bias; diversion from fundamentals
_____ Better distribution of effort among specialties

Remarks on reasons for your responses:

❊   ❊   ❊   ❊

The sample of university department heads to whom the questionnaire was sent was selected in an effort to meet the following criteria:

(a) representative mixture of large and small departments (as measured by Ph.D. degrees granted annually in the field in question);

(b) representative geographic distribution of departments; and

(c) representative mixture of departments by their general reputation for quality.

The responses to the questionnaire were analyzed in an attempt to secure some ideas of the possible biases in the returns.

The department heads to whom questionnaires were sent, identified as responding or not responding, were as follows (an asterisk denotes a private university):

Biology

Response	No response
Baylor *	Brown *
Boston *	Catholic *
California Institute of Technology *	Northeastern *
Florida	Notre Dame *
Massachusetts Institute of Technology *	Princeton *
	Stanford *
New York University *	
New Mexico	
Oregon	
Purdue	

Chemistry

Response	No response
Arizona	Boston *
Arkansas	Buffalo *
Catholic *	California (Los Angeles)
California Institute of Technology *	Chicago *
California (Berkeley)	Colorado
California (Berkeley) a)	Delaware
Columbia *	Georgia Institute of Technology *
Cornell *	Georgetown *
Emory *	Harvard *
Fordham *	Johns Hopkins *
George Washington *	Illinois
Illinois	Indiana
Louisville	Iowa State
Massachusetts	Kansas
Minnesota	Maryland
Nebraska	Massachusetts Institute of Technology *
Ohio State	Michigan
Pennsylvania *	North Carolina

Rutgers	Northeastern *
Southern California *	Notre Dame *
	Pennsylvania State
Texas A. and M.	Southern California *
Tulane *	Stanford *
Wisconsin	Syracuse *
West Virginia	Texas
	Wisconsin

a) Biochemistry

Physics

Response	No response
Brown *	Bryn Mawr *
California (Berkeley)	California Institute of Technology *
Carnegie Institute of Technology *	California (Los Angeles)
Colorado	Columbia *
Connecticut	Dayton
Cornell *	Harvard *
Johns Hopkins *	Illinois
Illinois	Iowa State
Indiana	Lehigh
Michigan	Maryland
North Carolina	Massachusetts Institute of Technology *
Ohio State	Minnesota
Oregon	Missouri
Princeton *	New York University *
Purdue	Northeastern *
Southern California	Rochester *
Texas A. and M.	Stanford *
Washington	St. Louis
Wisconsin	Texas
	Tennessee

Mathematics

Response	No response
Brown *	California Institute
California	of Technology *
(Los Angeles)	Colorado
Georgia	Florida
Illinois	Harvard *
Minnesota	Maryland
Notre Dame *	Michigan
Oklahoma	Northeastern *
Princeton *	Oklahoma A. and
Purdue	M.
Syracuse *	St. Louis *
Washington	Utah
Wisconsin	

Bacteriology

Response	No response
California (Berke-	California
ley)	(Los Angeles)
George Washing-	Cincinnati
ton *	Minnesota
Illinois	Ohio State
Maryland	Tennessee
Rochester *	
Texas	
Utah	
Wisconsin	

Psychology

Response	No response
Boston *	Claremont *
Brown *	Florida
California	Fordham *
(Los Angeles)	Kentucky
Chicago *	Michigan
Denver *	New York Univer-
Illinois	sity *
Indiana	North Carolina
Louisiana State	Oklahoma
Minnesota	Pittsburgh *
Missouri	Rochester *
Northeastern	Syracuse *
Ohio State	Tennessee
Oregon	Tulane *
Princeton *	Washington *
Purdue	Western Reserve *
Texas	

Geology

Response	No response
Columbia *	Chicago *
Illinois	Pittsburgh *
Massachusetts	St. Louis *
Institute of	
Technology *	
Wisconsin	

Engineering

Response	No response
California	Carnegie Institute
Institute of	of Technology *
Technology *	Cornell *
Columbia *	Illinois Institute of
Harvard *	Technology
Johns Hopkins *	Massachusetts
Northeastern *	Institute of
Purdue	Technology *
Stanford *	Michigan
Wisconsin	Washington

The lists above are summarized in Table A–15.

On looking at the lists and the table of departments which did and those which did not respond, it seems to me that there is no pattern which would indicate a bias. The proportion of persons who responded was higher in some fields than in others. As reported in Chapter 7, however, there is no relation between the proportion of responses among fields and attitudes by field. The proportion of responses was somewhat higher among public than among private schools, but this was not invariably true in each field.

The center of the question of bias introduced by nonresponse is, of course, the persons who did not respond. If the views of the respondents differ markedly from those of the nonrespondents, the tabulated responses present an incorrect picture of the attitude of department heads. Whether such a bias existed or not cannot be proved. My view is that response or non-response was primarily a matter of the attitudes of department heads towards the significance of the question under study, and of the time they were willing to spend to help a graduate student write a dissertation.

In short, I think that the sample of respondents was representative enough of academic opinion to be reliable as a guide to judgment, even though this cannot be demonstrated.

The department heads who responded were responsible for departments which granted almost 30 percent of all Ph.D. degrees granted in the selected fields in 1955 (Table A–16).

Even if the sample were mildly biased, the respondents are a group with heavy responsibilities for the training of a substantial proportion of the Ph.D.'s in important fields of science in the United States.

Notes

CHAPTER 1

1. President's Science Advisory Committee, *Strengthening American science, a report to the President* (Washington: Government Printing Office, 1958), p. 1.
2. *Ibid.*, p. 10.
3. National Science Foundation, *Federal grants and contracts for unclassified research in the life sciences, fiscal year 1955* (Washington: Government Printing Office, 1956).

From this publication are drawn the following examples of investigators in the life sciences receiving support from more than one federal agency:

Investigator and university	Title of investigation	Supporting agency *
Green, D. E. (Wisconsin)	Effect of radiation on enzymes	AEC
	Metalloflavoproteins	NIH
	Enzyme activity in nonmitochondrial system of pig heart	NIH
	Inhibition of enzymatic activity in foodstuffs	AQM
Lauffer, M. A. (Pittsburgh)	Radiation effect and physiochemical changes in viruses	AEC
	Atherosclerosis, characterization of blood lipoproteins	NIH
	Biophysical characterization of lipoproteins	NIH
	Biophysical investigations of bacteriophages	ONR
	Biophysical studies of plant viruses	NSF
Nord, F. F.	Enzymatic degradation of native and chemically modified proteins	AEC
	Natural pigments and mechanism of fat formation in micro-organisms	NIH

251

Investigator and university	Title of investigation	Supporting agency
Nord, F. F.	Mold pigments	ONR
	Structural, biochemical and physiochemical studies of lignin	NSF

* AEC, Atomic Energy Commission
NIH, National Institutes of Health
AQM, Army Quartermaster Corps
ONR, Office of Naval Research
NSF, National Science Foundation.

Without precise knowledge of the investigator and his laboratory, it is impossible to tell whether the grant or contract is for his personal work or for his laboratory in his name. The latter is common practice not only because some investigators are in general charge of the work of large groups, but also because the chance of obtaining funds is sometimes greater if a well-known person signs the application. Many applications are in the name of senior investigators who may not be deeply involved in the work. This custom complicates the problem of awarding grants and contracts and of assessing the effects of the funds on the development of man power.

4. National Science Foundation, *Seventh annual report*, 1957 (Washington: Government Printing Office, 1958), pp. 143–144; United States Atomic Energy Commission, *Major activities in the atomic energy programs July–December, 1956* (Washington: Government Printing Office, 1957), pp. 305–306.

Extensive lists of research projects indistinguishable by any criteria from those supported by the National Science Foundation can be compiled from the publications of each major federal research agency.

One such list is presented below, and the reader might, before referring to the footnote, attempt to tell which projects are supported by NSF and which by AEC:

Subject	University	Investigator
Theoretical research in elementary particle theory	Chicago	G. Wentzel
Research in theoretical physics	California (Berkeley)	D. S. Saxon *
Nuclear moments	California (Berkeley)	C. D. Jeffries
Excited levels of low mass nuclei	Kansas	L. W. Seagondollar *
Linac component development	Stanford	E. L. Ginzton
Nuclear spectroscopy	Ohio	J. N. Cooper
Theory of conductivity in quantum mechanics	Wisconsin	K. M. Watson *

Notes

Subject	University	Investigator
Precision beta-ray spectros-copy	Vanderbilt	S. K. Haynes
Neutron spectra and energy levels	Haverford College	Ajzenberg-Selove *
Low temperature research	Wisconsin	J. R. Dillinger

* Grants from the National Science Foundation; others from the Atomic Energy Commission.

5. C. Hitch, *The character of research and development in a competitive economy: Proceedings of a Conference on the Economic Effects of Research and Development sponsored by the National Science Foundation* (Washington: Government Printing Office, 1958), pp. 132–133.

6. *Congressional Record*, 4 May 1952, pp. 4387, 4596.

7. American Council on Education, *Sponsored research policy of colleges and universities*, report of the Committee on Institutional Research Policy (Washington: American Council on Education, 1954), p. 20.

8. National Science Foundation, National Science Foundation policy on co-ordination of basic research, Washington, D.C., 12 October 1956. Mimeographed.

9. Department of Health, Education and Welfare, *The advancement of medical research and education through the Department of Health, Education and Welfare*, final report of the Secretary's Consultants on Medical Research and Education (Washington: Government Printing Office, 1958), p. 35.

10. National Science Foundation, *Fifth annual report*, 1955 (Washington: Government Printing Office, 1955), pp. vii–viii.

11. United States House of Representatives, Hearing before the subcommittee of the Committee on Appropriations of the 84th Congress, 2d Session, on Independent Offices Appropriations for 1957.

12. United States House of Representatives Committee on Appropriations of the 84th Congress, 2d Session, Report on Independent Offices Appropriation for 1957, p. 48.

13. *Science and public policy, a program for the nation*, the report of the President's Scientific Research Board (Washington: Government Printing Office, 1947), vol. 1, p. 65.

14. Letter of 5 December 1957, from B. T. Shaw, Chairman, Interdepartmental Committee on Scientific Research and Development, to President Eisenhower, p. 6. Mimeographed.

15. *NSF policy on coordination.*

16. NSF, *Fifth annual report.*

17. J. R. Killian, "Science and public policy," *Science 129*, 130 (1959).

CHAPTER 2

1. J. D. Millett, *Financing higher education in the United States* (New York: Columbia University Press, 1952), p. 28.

2. California Institute of Technology, *Annual Report, 1948–49* (Pasadena: California Institute of Technology, 1950), p. 9.

3. A. Flexner, *Universities: American, British and German* (London: Oxford University Press, 1931).

4. V. Bush, *Science, the endless frontier, a report to the President* (Washington: Government Printing Office, 1945), p. 14.

5. Department of Scientific and Industrial Research, *D.S.I.R., a description of the work of the Department of Scientific and Industrial Research* (London: Her Majesty's Stationery Office, 1949), pp. 38–39.

6. *Annual Report of the Advisory Council on Scientific Policy 1956–1957* (London: Her Majesty's Stationery Office, 1957), Cmmd. 278, p. 8.

7. Pennsylvania State College, Engineering Experiment Station, *Proceedings of the Conference on Administration of Research, 12–14 September 1949*, Technical Bulletin no. 31 (State College, Pa., 1950), pp. 38–39.

8. C. E. K. Mees and J. A. Leermakers, *The organization of industrial scientific research* (New York: McGraw-Hill, 1950), p. 14.

9. E. E. Lape, *Medical research: a midcentury survey*, (Boston: Little, Brown, 1955), vol. 1, p. 117.

10. University of California, *The University of California in the next ten years: Report of a Study Committee on Contract Research* (Berkeley: University of California, 1950), p. 22.

11. U.S. House of Representatives, Committee on Government Operations, "The Riehlman Report," on the organization and administration of the military research and development program, House Report no. 2618, 83d Congress, 2d Session, 4 August 1954, p. 51.

12. H. W. Dodds, "Project research," *American Scientist 42*, 129 (1954).

CHAPTER 3

1. National Science Foundation. *Proceedings of a conference on research and development and its impact on the economy.* (Washington: Government Printing Office, 1958), pp. 1, 161.

Statistics on research and development expenditures in this country are not precise, and with successive refinements the estimates tend to rise. The available estimates for all years before 1953 seriously underestimate industrial research expenditures, as has been shown by a National Science Foundation survey, *Science and engineering in American industry, 1953–1954* (Washington: Government Printing Office, 1955), p. 3. It is not possible to correct the estimates for earlier years. Data for earlier years are shown only to give an idea of orders of magnitude. Federal expenditures have also been underestimated, largely because of underreporting of Department of Defense research and development expenditures buried in procurement funds and because pay and allowances to military personnel engaged in research and development were not reported as research and development expenditures for years before 1954. It is impossible to correct these underestimates for earlier years.

The lag in developing precise estimates is attributable primarily to the fact that there was little demand for the figures before World War II. Despite weaknesses in the estimates, they are accurate as indications of orders of magnitude; the estimates of federal obligations and expenditures in recent years are reasonably accurate when allowance is made for the underreporting of research and development expenditures buried in procurement funds. In this chapter, obligations are used at some points, and expenditures are used at others, to describe the federal effort. This is necessary because some important relations have been worked out in terms of obligations and others in terms of expenditures. As contrasted with many other types of federal expenditures, there are generally not wide variations between obligations and expenditures for research and developmnt in any given year. From 1948 to 1955, obligations ranged between 87 and 104 percent of expenditures.

2. *The budget of the United States for fiscal year 1960* (Washington: Government Printing Office, 1959), pp. 990.

3. National Science Foundation, *Government university relationships in federally sponsored scientific research and development.* (Washington: Government Printing Office, 1958), p. 6.

4. 1960 U.S. budget, p. 993.

5. J. A. Shannon and C. V. Kidd, "Medical research in perspective," *Science, 124,* 1187 (1956).

6. J. D. Millett, *Financing higher education in the United States* (New York: Columbia University Press, 1952), pp. 106–108, 178–188.

7. American Council on Education, *Sponsored research policy of colleges and universities, a report of the Committee on Institutional Research Policy* (Washington: American Council on Education, 1954), p. 30.

8. National Science Foundation, *Scientific activities for research and development in colleges and universities — expenditures and manpower, 1953–1954* (Washington: Government Printing Office, 1959).

9. Carnegie Foundation for the Advancement of Teaching, *Annual report for 1956–1957* (New York: Carnegie Foundation for the Advancement of Teaching, 1958), p. 12.

10. Unpublished tabulation prepared by the Division of Research Grants and Fellowships, National Institutes of Health.

11. NSF, *Expenditures and manpower, 1953–1954.*

12. 1930–1939: E. V. Hollis, *Towards improving Ph.D. programs* (Washington: American Council on Education, 1940).

1947–48 and 1954–55: Office of Education, *Earned degrees conferred by higher educational institutions* (Washington: Government Printing Office, 1950 and 1957).

The awarding of degrees of doctor of philosophy, in total and in the physical sciences, has always been highly concentrated in this country, although there seems to be a long-run trend towards dispersion. Thirty-three percent of all Ph.D.'s in science were awarded by the five universities granting the largest number of degrees over the period of 1930–1939, but the top five universities granted only 24 percent of the degrees in 1954–55. The decline of concentration of Ph.D. degrees in physics, chemistry, biochemistry, and mathematics is comparable, and a similar tendency toward dispersion exists in all fields except biochemistry. While the decrease in concentration might have been even more marked had it not been for federal research funds, this seems unlikely.

The stability of the lists of the five universities awarding the most Ph.D. degrees and the five awarding the next highest number is remarkable. For example, from 1930 to 1939 and in 1954–55, the California and Massachusetts Institutes of Technology, and Michigan, California, Chicago, Wisconsin, Columbia, Harvard, and Yale Universities granted the greatest number of Ph.D. degrees in physics. Illinois, Columbia, Wisconsin, Chicago, Ohio State, Johns Hopkins, M.I.T., Cornell, Yale and Minnesota granted the greatest number of Ph.D. degrees in chemistry from 1936 to 1939 and in 1954–55.

13. National Science Foundation, *Federal funds for science* (Washington: Government Printing Office, 1944), vol. 1, p. 45.

14. L. A. DuBridge, "Scientists and engineers: quantity plus quality," *Science 124*, 302 (1956).

CHAPTER 4

1. National Science Foundation, *Scientific activities for research and development in colleges and universities — expenditures and manpower, 1953–1954*, (Washington: Government Printing Office, 1959). While these data are for the academic year 1953–54, the salient relation — particularly the significance of the federal funds — has not changed.

2. This section is a condensed version of my article, "Basic research, description vs. definition," which appeared in *Science 129*, 368 (1959).

3. National Science Foundation, *Basic research, a national resource* (Washington: Government Printing Office, 1957), p. 25.

4. National Science Foundation, *Federal funds for science, fiscal years 1957, 1958 and 1959* (Washington: Government Printing Office, 1959), p. 24.

5. I. B. Cohen, *Science, servant of man* (Boston: Little, Brown, 1958), p. 55.

Notes

6. A. M. Brues, The new emotionalism in research, *Bulletin of the Atomic Scientists, 11*, 344 (1955).

7. H. A. Shepard, Basic research and the social system of pure science, *Philosophy of Science, 23*, 57 (1956).

8. The Ford Foundation, *Annual report of 1958* (New York: The Ford Foundation, 1959), p. 94.

9. Unpublished, undated, mimeographed table made available to me by the Ford Foundation.

10. Harvard University, *The behavioral sciences at Harvard*, report by a faculty committee (Cambridge, Mass.: Harvard University, 1954), pp. 274–275.

11. House of Representatives, Hearings before a Subcommittee of the Committee on Interstate and Foreign Commerce, 79th Congress, 2d Session on the National Science Foundation Act, 28 and 29 May 1946, p. 13.

12. National Science Foundation, *Fifth annual report*, 1955 (Washington: Government Printing Office, 1956), p. 60.

13. NSF, *Expenditures and manpower, 1953–1954.*

14. D. Wolfle, *America's resources of specialized talent* (New York: Harper, 1954), pp. 44–46.

Wolfle observed that: "While there have been great percentage changes in bachelors' degrees by field since 1900, the distribution of doctors' degrees has remained much more constant. In fact, the comparative stability of doctors' degrees granted in the United States is impressive as are the large changes in the distribution of bachelors' degrees."

The difference between his observation of stability and mine of change may be accounted for in that the data for the later postwar years were not available to him and he assessed changes in the distribution of doctorates against much larger changes in the distribution of bachelors' degrees.

Data shedding some light on recent shifts in specialties within fields of natural science, based mostly on the distribution of all employed Ph.D.'s by field as compared with the distribution of graduate students by field in recent years, are available in the following:

(a) Federal Security Agency, *Manpower resources in physics, 1951*, Scientific Manpower Series no. 3 (Washington: Government Printing Office, 1952), pp. 15, 33, 40 (table 21).

(b) U.S. Department of Labor, *Manpower resources in chemistry and chemical engineering, 1951*, Bulletin No. 1132 (Washington: Government Printing Office, 1953), pp. 26, 52, 75 (table A–18).

(c) National Science Foundation, *Manpower resources in the biological sciences, 1951* (Washington: Government Printing Office, 1955), pp. 15, 48–51.

(d) National Science Foundation, *Manpower resources in mathematics, 1951* (Washington: Government Printing Office, 1955), pp. 11, 20 (tables 11A and 11B).

(e) National Science Foundation, *Manpower resources in the earth sciences, 1951* (Washington: Government Printing Office, 1954), pp. 24, 38 (table A–11).

(f) National Science Foundation, *Scientific personnel resources* (Washington: Government Printing Office, 1955), p. 72.

15. National Science Foundation, *Fourth conference on scientific manpower*, 121st meeting of the American Association for the Advancement of Science (Washington: Government Printing Office, 1954), p. 2.

CHAPTER 6

1. National Science Foundation, *Fifth annual report*, 1955 (Washington: Government Printing Office, 1956), p. 9.

2. H. W. Dodds, "Project research," *American Scientist 42*, 128–130 (1954).

3. J. E. Deitrick and R. C. Berson, *Medical schools in the United States at midcentury* (New York: McGraw-Hill, 1953), pp. 46–49.

A different point of view is expressed in J. A. Shannon and C. V. Kidd, "Medical research in perspective," *Science 124*, 1188 (1956):

The research-project approach can be pernicious if it provides short periods of support without assuring continuity, or if it applies overt or indirect pressure on the investigator to shift his interests to narrowly defined work set by the source of money, or if it imposes financial and scientific accounting in unreasonable detail.

After 10 years of experience in the administration of a system using the word "project" for the applications submitted by investigators, it appears that the evils noted in the previous paragraph can be and have been averted, primarily by attention to procedures centering around extension of the freedom of the investigator.

Freedom is extended by quite specific principles, devices, and actions — for example, by providing more funds for broadly defined areas of study and more support for research that is not directly related to a specific disease, by increasingly stable support; by freedom to change lines of inquiry; by freedom to shift the uses of budgeted funds; and by freedom from detailed reporting requirements.

4. American Council on Education, *Sponsored research policy of colleges and universities*, a report of the Committee on Institutional Research Policy (Washington: American Council on Education, 1954), p. 55.

5. C. P. Richter, "Free research versus design research," *Science 118*, 93 (1953).

6. University of North Carolina, *Survey of the behavioral sciences, 1953–54*, a report of the Visiting Committee, Chapel Hill, N. C., June 1954, p. 78. Dittoed.

7. H. Himsworth (ed.), *The support of medical research: A symposium organized by the Council for International Organizations of Medical Sciences*

Notes

(Springfield, Ill.: Charles C Thomas, 1956; Oxford: Blackwell Scientific Publications Ltd., 1956), pp. 23–24.

8. Press release of 4 April 1956 from the White House by James C. Hagerty, Press Secretary to the President, on a report of the Committee on Loyalty in Relation to Government Support of Unclassified Research of the National Academy of Sciences, 13 March 1956, p. 5.

CHAPTER 7

1. A. T. Waterman, "Government support of research," *Science 110*, 704 (1949).

2. National Science Foundation, *Graduate student enrollment and support in American universities and colleges, 1954* (Washington: Government Printing Office, 1957), pp. 7, 10, 35, 36, 273–275.

The counting of graduate students is a complicated business because of such problems as defining graduate students, securing complete reporting and estimating for underreporting, and fixing the time at which counts are made. These problems are discussed in detail in this National Science Foundation report, particularly in Appendix E. My objective has not been to make new and better estimates, but to select from existing studies those quantities that shed the most light on the questions under examination. I used a total of 217,000 graduate students, the estimate noted on p. 294 of this National Science Foundation report, and distributed this number by field in accordance with correction factors cited on p. 292 of the report.

3. D. Wolfle, *America's resources of specialized talent* (New York: Harper, 1954), pp. 204, 317.

4. Department of Health, Education and Welfare: Office of Education, *Earned degrees conferred by higher educational institutions, 1957–58* (Preliminary tabulations).

5. *The budget of the United States for fiscal year 1960.* (Washington: Government Printing Office, 1959), p. 996.

"It is estimated that 20,000 to 30,000 graduate students would be employed as research assistants in 1960."

The National Science Foundation estimated that there were only 10,800 research assistants in 1954. *Federal support for science students in higher education, 1954* (Washington: Government Printing Office, 1956), p. 12. Even allowing for undercounting in the Science Foundation survey, it is clear that the number of research assistants has grown rapidly.

6. The views of the eight department heads who believe both that the quality of training has declined and that the federal funds are responsible deserve special attention:

Department of Chemistry, California (Berkeley) — "While quality of training has decreased for the country as a whole, training has been improved in leading universities that have been able to use Federal funds wisely."

Department of Biochemistry, California (Berkeley) — "Change principally due to increased student numbers per staff member. Federal funds have increased this, but are not the principal factor in doing so."

Department of Chemistry, New York University — "Quality of training decreased somewhat for the country as a whole because of the availability of funds to weaker schools."

Department of Chemistry, Cornell — "Quality has decreased somewhat in spite of staff efforts due to acceptance by industry of all graduates regardless of ability and performance in graduate school."

Department of Chemistry, Minnesota — "The percentage of top quality graduate students has declined in chemistry."

Department of Physics, Oregon — "Preoccupation with research contracts and too large enrollments have had a deteriorating effect."

Department of Bacteriology, George Washington — "Training more specialized and less general, particularly since the grants tend to focus thoughts on a restricted aspect of the field."

Department of Bacteriology, Wisconsin — "This was a faculty vote. Four faculty members thought the quality of training had increased somewhat; six thought there has been somewhat of a decrease."

CHAPTER 8

1. National Science Foundation, *Faculty scientific research activities at colleges and universities, 1953–54, reviews of data on research and development* (Washington: Government Printing Office, 1957), p. 2. This report cited 62,000 total faculty members and 55,000 full-time equivalents. I increased the figures moderately to approximate the situation in 1958.

2. National Education Association, *Teacher supply and demand in colleges and universities, 1955–56 and 1956–57* (Washington: National Education Association, 1957), p. 24.

In an attempt to refine the meaning of "supply of," "demand for," and "shortage of" teachers, I undertook to track down information on such matters as student-faculty ratios, and data on the proportion of faculty time spent on research, only to come to the conclusion that (a) the data are inadequate and (b) if the data were adequate, they would not answer any important questions. The most exhaustive treatment of the demand supply question is to be found in D. M. Blank and G. V. Stigler, *The demand and supply of scientific personnel* (New York: National Bureau of Economic Research, 1957), p. 95.

3. *Journal of the American Medical Association 168*, 1599 (1958).

4. National Education Association, *Salaries paid and salary practices in universities, colleges and junior colleges, 1957–58* (Washington: National Education Association, 1958), p. 12.

5. National Science Foundation, *Proceedings of a conference on research*

and development and its impact on the economy (Washington: Government Printing Office, 1958), p. 4.

6. National Education Association, *Salaries paid and salary practices in universities, colleges and junior colleges, 1955–56*, Research Bulletin, vol. 34, no. 3 (Washington: National Education Association, 1956), p. 113.

7. L. S. Kubie, "Some unsolved problems of the scientific career," *American Scientist 42*, 106 (1954).

8. NSF, *Salaries paid*, p. 43.

9. National Science Foundation, *Fourth annual report*, 1954 (Washington: Government Printing Office, 1954), p. 24.

10. Carnegie Corporation of New York, *Reports of officers for the fiscal year ended September 30, 1952* (New York: Carnegie Corporation, 1953), p. 18.

11. H. E. Longenecker, *University faculty compensation policies and practices in the United States*, a study for the Association of American Universities (Urbana: University of Illinois Press, 1956), pp. 77, 191–262.

In Chapter VI of this study, it is reported that:

Three of the [24] institutions visited permitted extra compensation for participation in research during the academic year. One of these has sought to maintain the principle of full time service while permitting additional compensation to a minimum of 25 percent of the budgeted rate. No indication of a limitation on additional compensation was apparent in another; and in the third, extra compensation could be derived up to 20 percent of the budgeted rate but only by agreement to undertake no work outside the institution concurrently and also within a total limitation on all earnings from the institution itself and to four-thirds of the budgeted annual salary during a 12 month period.

Officials of other universities have discussed with me their practice of permitting faculty members to earn income from federal research contracts during the academic year. One large university, for example, has permitted faculty members whose research contracts are administered by a central university research organization to be paid at the rate of $.90 an hour for each $1,000 of annual salary earned during the school year. Thus, a faculty member earning $10,000 a year would be paid $9.00 an hour for work on research contracts with a maximum of eight hours a week. All such overtime research by faculty members was entered on time cards, and the payroll was reviewed by the office of the president. If it appeared that a faculty member was spending more overtime than he should on contract research work, the president's office called the appropriate dean, and the situation was kept under control. The president and his staff were considering a drastic modification of university policy with regard to outside employment during the academic year.

12. Princeton University, *The President's Report 1957–58* (Princeton: Princeton University Press, 1958), p. 9.

13. Longenecker, pp. 191–262.

14. Carnegie Foundation for the Advancement of Teaching, *The financial status of the professor in America and in Germany*, Bulletin no. 2 (1908), p. 7.

15. National Science Foundation, *University relationships in federally sponsored scientific research and development* (Washington: Government Printing Office, 1958), p. 26.

16. Longenecker, pp. 191–262.

17. National Science Foundation, *Scientific activities for research and development in colleges and universities — expenditures and manpower, 1953–54* (Washington: Government Printing Office, 1959), p. 66. At least 4,500 persons were professional research employees in 1953–54 and the number undoubtedly increased to more than 5,000 by 1959.

18. The following examples of practices in individual universities drawn from the *Review of current research and directory of member institutions, 1955*, compiled and published by the American Society for Engineering Education, show how the nonfaculty scientists are scattered through universities.

Northwestern University — "Approximately 125 persons are engaged in full or part-time research of whom about one third are on the academic staff. Another third are employed specifically for research, nearly all on government contracts. The remainder are graduate students, some on contracts but mostly on university sponsored research associated with graduate study."

Princeton University — "Those engaged in research either full or part time include 25 faculty members, 40 graduate students, 65 other professional personnel and 50 non-academic technicians, mechanics, etc."

The Massachusetts Institute of Technology — "Most faculty members (over 475) and graduate students (nearly 2,000) are active in one or more research projects. In addition, a staff of professional workers (numbering about 500) is active on sponsored research administered through the Division of Industrial Cooperation.

CHAPTER 9

1. American Council on Education, *College and university business administration*, compiled by the National Committee on the preparation of a Manual on College and University Business Administration (Washington: American Council on Education, 1955), Vol. 2, pp. 140–149.

2. V. Bush, *Science, the endless frontier: A report to the President* (Washington: Government Printing Office, 1945), p. 32.

3. D. D. Eisenhower, Memorandum for directors and chiefs of War Department general and special staff divisions and bureaus and the commanding generals of the major commands on the subject: Scientific and techno-

logical resources as military assets (April 30, 1946), cited in D. Price, *Government and science* (New York: New York University Press, 1954), p. 57.

4. U.S. House of Representatives Committee on Government Operations, "The Riehlman Report," on the organization and administration of the military research and development program, House Report no. 2618, 83rd Congress, 2d Session, 4 August 1954, p. 13.

5. While the areas of misunderstanding, incompatibility, and irritation created by the procurement approach to research have narrowed substantially over the years, problems still exist. Some of them are acute, as indicated by these examples of statements made to me by university people:

We will refuse to deal further with ——— because they are pests. The ——— placed demands upon the university which would require them to change their insurance policies and their accounting set-up. They switch personnel so rapidly that the university never knows who it is dealing with. They have a super-structure of auditors, checkers, etc., who are merely a bother and contribute nothing to the ——— or to the university. The ——— contract with the university is 43 pages long, while the average ONR contract is 3 or 4 pages long. — Administrator in a state university

The university is in constant difficulty with the ——— particularly. There are often delays of several months after contract proposals are submitted to the ——— by the university. Then the ——— complains if the university takes a week before returning the signed contract. This difficulty arises because the initial responsibility for the handling of contracts is delegated to people at a low level. Then the contract proposals have to move up the hierarchy. If at any step on this ladder an objection is raised or a change proposed the proposal returns to the bottom of the ladder to work its way up again. — Administrator in a private university

6. National Science Foundation. *Government university relationships in federally sponsored scientific research and development.* (Washington: Government Printing Office, 1958), p. 30.

7. Engineering College Research Council, *Engineering college research review, 1957* (New York: American Society for Engineering Education, 1957). The following example drawn from this volume indicates the variety of administrative tasks performed by these unincorporated research institutes:

The director of the Research Division of the New York University College of Engineering is charged with the promotion and administration of sponsored research projects, especially with industry and government agencies. He collaborates with department chairmen in organizing such projects and in preparing contracts for them, and he acts for the Dean in administering them. Members of the faculty and regular staff of the College of Engineering usually direct and/or are employed on sponsored research projects; such activities are considered as part of their regular duties (p. 190).

8. Engineering College Research Council. *Review of current research and directory of member institutions, 1955.* (State College, Pa.: American Society for Engineering Education, 1956), p. 180.

9. American Council on Education, vol. 2, pp. 135–136.

10. Pennsylvania State College, Engineering Experiment Station, *Proceedings of the conference on administration of research, September 12–14, 1949.* Technical Bulletin no. 31 (State College, Pa., 1950), p. 19.

11. H. H. Good, "Administration of sponsored research," in *Scientific research: its administration and organization* by G. P. Bush and L. H. Hattery (Washington: American University Press, 1950), pp. 12–14.

12. Parts of this section are drawn from C. V. Kidd, "Research planning and research policy; scientists and administrators," *Science 118*, 3058 (1953).

13. A. T. Waterman, "Government support of research," *Science 110*, 705 (1949).

14. The following formal expression of opinion by the faculty of the University of California is not unique, and it states the general path of development of administrative sophistication in most universities as experience with federal contracts has accumulated:

In matters with which the office of the Vice-President and the office of Business Affairs are concerned there are areas of activity which could effectively employ a regularly established advisory body of the faculty. The business offices are constantly drawing up new rules and deciding on procedures, many of which have a direct bearing on educational policy, and the faculty are required to fit themselves into these patterns although they have had little opportunity to assist in formulating them. The Budget Officer of the University, dealing frequently with the actual selection of items for which funds are or are not to be allocated, could well utilize faculty advice beyond that which is available in the explanatory statement submitted with the budget proposals. Departmental chairmen are constantly confused and confounded by the fact that policy decisions made within the department are ignored, replaced, or modified by someone higher in the administration — often the business office. These are not the two-way channels of communication which would ensure that the faculty's thinking has been given due consideration, nor are the members of the department concerned given reasons why its plans and recommendations were not followed. On the other hand, this committee would be remiss if it failed to acknowledge that where specific consideration is requested of the many members of the business offices, sympathetic, energetic, and often indispensable action results whenever it is possible. Evidently the difficulties develop only in the formative stages of policies, and rarely in the execution of such policies.

University of California, "The faculty and the educational policies of the university," in *Proceedings of the University of California Eighth All-University Faculty Conference, Davis Campus, April 30, May 1 and 2, 1953.* (Berkeley: University of California Press, 1953), p. 31.

CHAPTER 10

1. J. A. Stratton, "Research and the university," *Chemical and Engineering News 31*, 2582 (1953).

2. H. W. Dodds, "Project research," *American Scientist 42*, 128 (1954).

3. P. E. Klopsteg, "University responsibilities and government money," *Science 124*, 920 (1956).

4. W. H. Whyte, *The organization man* (New York: Simon and Schuster, 1956), p. 221.

5. A. Gregg, "Medical institutes," an address in *Prospect and retrospect in neurology*, edited by the Staff of the Montreal Neurological Institute (Boston: Little, Brown, 1955), p. 15.

6. J. E. Deitrick and R. C. Berson, *Medical schools in the United States at midcentury* (New York: McGraw-Hill, 1953), p. 47.

7. M. A. Tuve, "Technology and national research policy," *Bulletin of the Atomic Scientists 9*, 291 (1953).

8. Gregg, p. 15.

9. National Science Foundation, *Government-university relationships in federally sponsored scientific research and development* (Washington: Government Printing Office, 1958), p. 29.

10. L. A. DuBridge, "Science and government," *Chemical and Engineering News 31*, 1389 (1953).

11. Pennsylvania State College, Engineering Experiment Station, *Proceedings of the Conference on Administration of Research, September 12–14, 1949*, Technical Bulletin no. 31 (State College, Pa., 1950), p. 30.

12. A. T. Waterman, "Government support of research," *Science 110*, 708 (1949).

CHAPTER 11

1. A. H. Dupree, *Science in the federal government* (Cambridge, Mass.: Harvard University Press, 1957), p. 14.

2. National Science Foundation, *Advisory and coordinating mechanisms for federal research and development, 1956–57* (Washington: Government Prniting Office, 1957).

3. C. P. Richter, "Free research versus design research," *Science 118*, 91 (1953).

4. United States Atomic Energy Commission, *In the matter of J. Robert Oppenheimer*, transcript of hearings before the Personnel Security Board, 12 April 1952 through 6 May 1954 (Washington: Government Printing Office, 1954).

5. D. Price, *Government and science* (New York: New York University Press, 1954), p. 143.

6. Richter, p. 91.

7. C. A. Mills, "Distribution of American research funds," *Science 116*, 127 (1948).

8. W. H. Whyte, *The organization man* (New York: Simon and Schuster, 1957), p. 223.

CHAPTER 12

1. M. Polanyi, *The logic of liberty* (Chicago: University of Chicago Press, 1951), p. 90.

2. J. P. Bernal, *The social function of science* (New York: Macmillan, 1939; London: Routledge & Kegan Paul Ltd., 1939), p. 415.

3. L. Hogben, *Science for the citizen* (New York: W. W. Norton, 1951; London: George Allen & Unwin Ltd., 1951), p. 741.

4. G. Sarton, *The history of science and the new humanism* (New York: Braziller, 1956), p. 177.

5. A. de Tocqueville, *Democracy in America* (New York: A. A. Knopf, 1946), vol. 2, pp. 41–47.

6. P. E. Klopsteg, "University responsibilities and government money," *Science 124*, 920 (1956).

7. J. D. Millett, *Financing higher education in the United States* (New York: Columbia University Press, 1952), p. 355.

8. A. H. Dupree, *Science in the federal government* (Cambridge, Mass.: Harvard University Press, 1957).

9. J. R. Baker, *Science and the planned state* (New York: Macmillan, 1945; London: George Allen & Unwin Ltd., 1945), p. 53.

10. I. B. Cohen, *Science, servant of man* (Boston: Little, Brown, 1948), p. 32.

11. H. W. Dodds, L. M. Hacker, and L. Rogers, *Government assistance to universities in Great Britain* (New York: Columbia University Press, 1952), p. 113.

12. D. Price, *Government and science* (New York: New York University Press, 1954), p. 84.

13. *Sixth annual report of the Advisory Council on Scientific Policy (1952–53)*, report on the exploitation of science by industry (London: Her Majesty's Stationery Office, 1954), Cmmd. 8874, p. 1.

14. J. A. Stratton, "Research and the university," *Chemical and Engineering News 31*, 2582 (June 22, 1953).

15. *Science and Technology Acts of 1958*, Analysis and summary prepared by the staff and submitted to the Senate Committee on Government Operations on S.3126: A Bill to Create a Department of Science and Technology (Washington: Government Printing Office, 1958). While the staff arguments for creation of the Department seem strained, the document contains comprehensive references to the question of a Federal Department of Science.

Notes

In contrast, Lloyd Berkner's proposal, "Government sponsorship of scientific research," *Science 129*, 817 (1959), for a Department of Science whose function would not be the formulation of science policy at the top but rather strengthening "governmental scientific and technical services not principally involved in attaining existing department objectives or strongly related in the organic sense to the functions of a single federal department but of the utmost importance to the Government and the people as a whole" is sound and should in my opinion be adopted. The only significant objection to the proposal, which Berkner pointed out, is that "Congress would end by dumping all the scientific activities of the departments and agencies into such a department," a move that "would, of course, be little short of catastrophic."

16. National Science Foundation. *Seventh annual report*, 1957 (Washington: Government Printing Office, 1958), p. 56.

17. J. R. Killian, "Science and public policy," *Science 129*, 134 (January 16, 1959).

18. A. MacLeish, "What is a true university?" *The Saturday Review* (January 31, 1959), p. 13.

19. Carnegie Foundation for the Advancement of Teaching, *Annual Report for 1956–57*: Summary of a discussion by the trustees on federal programs for higher education (New York: Carnegie Foundation for the Advancement of Teaching, 1957), p. 16.

Index

Index

Mathematics, 126, 128, 144
McElroy, N., 13
Medical schools: income and expenditure, 48–50; special problems, 51, 142
Mees, C. E. K., 31
Mellon Institute, 162
Meteorology, 226
Michigan, University of, 54, 128, 179
Microwave Laboratory, 179
Millett, J. D., 25, 49
Mills, C. A., 199
Minnesota, University of, 54, 55, 69, 128, 134
Morrill Act of 1890, 189

National Aeronautics and Space Agency and Council, 23, 42
National Academy of Sciences–National Research Council, 120, 189, 190, 225
National Advisory Committee on Aeronautics, 56
National Advisory Councils (Public Health Service), 192
National Defense Education Act of 1958, 227
National Education Association, 143
National Fund for Medical Education, 99
National Institutes of Health: indirect cost policy, 51, 98; research authority and grants, 10, 54, 113; scientific advisers, 192, 194; training activities, 16, 223
National research policy, 18–24, 219–231
National Science Board, 22
National Science Foundation: basic research definitions, 64; charters and policies, 3, 4, 8–23, 104, 120, 155, 159, 183, 224, 226; Divisional Committees, 191, 192; expenditures, 42–46, 54–56; policy functions, 20–22, 223; project system, 108; social science support, 71, 73, 74; training activities, 16, 223
National Security Council, 23
Naval Research Advisory Committee, 191
Navy, Department of: 178, 183, 191; Office of Naval Research, 4, 8, 10, 54, 191, 223
New York University, 55

Oceanography, 226

Office of Naval Research. *See* Navy, Department of
Office of Scientific Research of the Air Research and Development Command, 192
Office of Scientific Research and Development, 157, 190
Ohio State University, 160
Ohio State University Research Foundation, 160
Oppenheimer, J. Robert, In the matter of, 195
Overhead costs, 93–98
Overlapping of research, 10, 11

Pennsylvania, University of, 54, 55
Ph.D's: by field, 74; forces affecting choice of field, 74–79; intelligence, 126
Physical sciences: financing, 53, 63; scientific training, 126, 128, 140, 141
Polanyi, M., 206
President's Science Advisory Committee, 2, 5, 22, 224
Price, D. K., 196, 220
Princeton University, 54, 164
Professional research employees, 152–154, 227
Project: East River, 196; Hartwell, 196; Lincoln, 183, 196; Vista, 196
Psychology, 53, 127, 141
Public Health Service: research authority and policies, 3, 8, 15, 104, 120; research funds, 44, 55, 56; scientific advisers, 191, 192
Purchase of research, 5–9
Purdue University, 128, 137

Radiation Laboratory, 177, 178, 183, 184, 185, 186
Rand Corporation, 11, 177
Research: centralization and dispersion, 12, 13, 213; classification, 61–64; coordination, 20, 21, 222–225; cost participation by universities, 84–93; costs, 83–102; indirect costs, 93–98; national policy, 18–24, 219–231; overlapping and duplication, 10, 11; purchase and support, 5–9; secrecy, 117–122; *see also* Basic research
Research assistants: dissertations, 132; distribution by field, 129; general, 80, 128; nature of work, 129; numbers and income of, 130

271